Avoiding Claims in Building Contracts

To Charlie Willis, Master Joiner, who, by example, taught me the true meaning of professionalism; to Fisher & Woods, Builders of Dovercourt, his employers, who inspired me with a love of good building; and to Mr Essenden, Disablement Registration Officer at the Hammersmith Labour Exchange, who rescued me and pointed me in the right direction at the end of the Second World War.

And to many friends in the building industry and its related professions.

Avoiding Claims in Building Contracts

Peter J. Lord-Smith
FRIBA, FCIOB, FCIArb, FFB

Published in Association with Kennedys

Butterworth Architecture
An imprint of Butterworth-Heinemann Ltd
Linacre House, Jordan Hill, Oxford OX2 8DP

ℛ A member of the Reed Elsevier Group

OXFORD   LONDON   BOSTON
MUNICH   NEW DELHI   SINGAPORE   SYDNEY
TOKYO   TORONTO   WELLINGTON

First published 1994

British Library Cataloguing in Publication Data
Lord-Smith, Peter J.
   Avoiding Claims in Building Contracts
   I. Title
   344.10378624

ISBN 0 7506 1728 4

Composition by Genesis Typesetting, Rochester, Kent
Printed and bound in Great Britain

Contents

Preface

Various forms of contract are now currently in use, but the majority of contracts are still let on a 'lump-sum' basis. The general principles enunciated in this book will apply to all such lump-sum building contracts, where an Architect and a Quantity Surveyor are appointed as contractual officers. The relationships between the various persons, firms and companies involved in such contracts are shown in the diagram annexed hereto as Appendix 1.

For the sake of simplicity, the detail is related to the form of contract in most general use, namely the "Standard Form of Building Contract 1980", as variously amended (JCT80), which is published by RIBA Publications Limited at the request of the Joint Contracts 'Tribunal'.

The term 'claims' is, strictly speaking, incorrect, because it is not used in any of the Contracts or Sub-Contracts to which reference will be made. It is, however, a convenient form of shorthand in common use, and refers to all situations where a contractor (or a sub-contractor) considers himself to be entitled to compensation arising out of the terms of the contract (or sub-contract).

There are various types of 'claims', for instance when a Contractor or a Sub-Contractor considers that variations or the expenditure on Provisional Sums have not been properly measured and valued, or that certificates for payment are in inadequate amounts. These, however, are relatively straightforward matters, and are dealt with in various publications on the subject of quantity surveying.

This book is primarily concerned with 'claims' for additional time or money resulting from changes of various kinds which take place after a contract has been let. In this connection, the term 'claims' is incorrect because a contractor merely has to give "notice" or make an "application", and it is then for the contractual officers (Architect and/or Quantity Surveyor) to settle the issues raised. The term 'claims' might then be correctly used in relation to such action as a contractor may take in the event of his being dissatisfied with the decisions made by the contractual officers, and an unresolved dispute has arisen.

This book is not intended to be a legal reference – the author is not qualified for that task, and there are a number of authoritative books on that subject. Rather this is a study of the practical implications of claims in which the author has had extensive experience. This book is divided into chapters addressed to the various participants in building contracting, each chapter recommending the steps which that participant should take in order to avoid the necessity for the making of claims or, if they do occur, how to mitigate their effects.

Acknowledgements

I am very grateful to Mr R.H. Mildred, FRICS, FCIArb, FFB, Past Chairman of the Chartered Institute of Arbitrators, and Mr J.V. Redmond, Solicitor, of Messrs Laytons of Bristol, for reading the manuscript and for making valuable comments and suggestions as to the relevant law and practice. I am also grateful to Mrs Pamela Turner of Tewkesbury for having so efficiently undertaken the tedious task of checking the manuscript for grammar, syntax and spelling, and for making appropriate corrections.

Introduction

Fifty years ago, with Rommel at the gates of Egypt, and two years before the D-day invasion of Nazi Europe, the government under Winston Churchill was even then so confident of victory that it was turning its mind as to how to improve social conditions in post-war Britain. The best known result was the publication of the Report by Churchill's long time friend and colleague, Lord Beveridge, which led to the establishment of the National Health Service.

The government realised that after the war, the building industry would be faced with a very considerable challenge:

> When victory over Germany is won there will have been no building for peace purposes for more than five years; there will be bomb damage to be made good, a mass of deferred repairs and maintenance work, a demand for schools and for civic, industrial and commercial building, and finally, most important of all, an urgent and continuing demand for houses.

In December 1942, as a result of this concern, the then Minister of Works, the Rt Hon. Lord Portal DSO MVO, established a Committee comprising 41 distinguished members of the building industry and its related professions, under the chairmanship of Sir Ernest Simon, and with Mr G.A. Jellicoe FRIBA as a consultant.

The principal matter which the Committee was instructed to consider and report on was:

> To examine the whole question of the placing and management of building contracts; to consider how far existing practices are suitable, and to make recommendations to secure that building organisation shall be so improved as to provide the best possible service to the nation while maintaining an efficient and prosperous industry.

The Committee's Report was submitted to Lord Portal on the 20th May 1944. On his instructions, it was to be "made public without delay", and it was published under the title: 'The Placing and Management of Building Contracts', Report of the Central Council for Works and Buildings. The Report has since come to be known as the 'Simon' Report, after the name of its Chairman.

The Report started with a general survey of the pre-war building industry, its structure and standards. It then compared the difficulties faced by the building industry with those of other manufacturing industries, and came to the not surprising conclusion that:

> Compared with factory conditions having all the economies of efficient plant and machinery, of good supervision and good conditions of work and welfare, the problems are incomparably more difficult.[1]

The Report then set out what was considered to be good practice in placing a building contract,[2] followed by the most important finding in the Report, namely the reasons for inefficiency in building contracting. Bearing in mind that the majority of the Committee members were building professionals, and that the majority of those were architects, it might be thought surprising that there is no suggestion that building contractors were in any way responsible for inefficiency – on the contrary, it could all be traced to unsatisfactory practices by building owners and their architects:

> Any inefficiency can be traced to one or other of the following causes:
> (a) Insufficient pre-contract preparation of the particulars of the work to be carried out.
> (b) Extensive variation orders after the contract is placed.

This message was repeated in the 'Conclusions and Recommendations' Section I, 'The Placing of Contracts'.[3] It was followed in the first paragraph of Section II, 'The Building Owner', by the effects of inadequate pre-contract preparation:

> It makes it impossible for the general contractor to organise his work effectively; it is the cause of endless variations during the course of the work. The results are high costs and delays.[4]

As to it being impossible for the contractor to organise his work effectively, the Committee explained this in greater detail in the body of the Report:

> The contractor is liable to constant interference by alterations ordered by the architect on behalf of his client during the progress of the work. He also has to co-ordinate the work of many sub-contractors, often chosen not by himself but by the architect. There may be many sub-contractors working on a single

building, each employing his own labour. The co-ordination of these numerous gangs of men working under independent firms is a task of the utmost difficulty, unique to the building industry.[5]

A further factor, not mentioned by the Committee, is that contractors have several contracts running at the same time. Any delay or disruption on one or more of these contracts will inevitably affect his performance on all contracts, and this snowball effect can well cause him insuperable management difficulties, if not total management chaos. It is not at all surprising, therefore, that the Committee did not put any blame for inefficiency in the building industry on the shoulders of contractors.

In the second paragraph of Section II, 'The Building Owner', the Committee set out the way in which this inefficiency could, and should, be avoided:

> The building owner can prevent this. He should, with the architect, do his thinking in advance and should see that the work is not started on site until the whole job has been carefully thought out, and all requirements have been accurately defined in such detail as is necessary at this stage by drawings, specifications and bills of quantities.[6]

This had been dealt with in greater detail in Paragraphs 25 and 26 of the Report (Appendix 4), and, in Paragraph 26, it also explained the architect's duty to protect his client from the damage which will be caused to him as author of his own misfortunes:

> When the owner wishes to insist on undue hurry, the Architect should endeavour to convince him of the importance of having time to complete his drawings in detail.

Also in Paragraph 26 (Appendix 4), the Committee further absolved contractors from responsibility:

> The builder should also be in a position to insist on full particulars before starting work, but he is often not listened to ...

All these messages have been repeated over the years since the 'Simon' Report was published, by further government reports, and by recommendations in publications by the Royal Institute of British Architects (RIBA), and others, and by the National Consultative Committee for Building (NJCC), which are referred to where appropriate in the body of this book.

Incredibly, despite all these publications, requirements and recommendations, inadequate pre-contract preparation is still the norm, as most contractors, and indeed quantity surveyors, would be able, if not willing for reasons of policy, to confirm!

The direct damage to building owners is, as the 'Simon' Report says, "high costs and delays". In other words, they get their buildings later than need have been the case, and they will have to make additional payments to the contractor as compensation for what in the industry is charmingly referred to as the 'buggeration factor'. But one can hardly feel sorry for building owners because, as the 'Simon' Report also says, "He can prevent it if he wishes".

There is, however, one reason why one can feel sorry for building owners, and this is because of a hidden on-cost depending on which architects they employ, as was explained by a leading speaker at a conference:

> Dare I tell you that we Builders not only price the Bill of Quantities – we also price the Architect, so that one with a reputation for efficiency and fair play will produce a lower tender for his Client.[7]

One should always feel sorry for genuine contractors, because they are frequently accused of being inefficient, often by the very people who are responsible for inducing inefficiency! And also because they frequently suffer financial losses by being deprived of their true entitlements to compensation by architects through ignorance of their duties, and sometimes, aided and abetted by quantity surveyors, by being over-zealous in misguided attempts to protect their clients, or in order to protect themselves from negligence actions where they have been the cause of inadequate pre-contract preparation and its consequences.

However, it must regrettably be mentioned in passing that not all contractors are 'genuine'; there are some that can only be described as 'unscrupulous' and who, having sophisticated claims departments, will exploit the technique of 'pricing the architect' to their advantage. They will deliberately underprice their tenders in the certain knowledge that they will be able to recover the under-pricing, and make excess profits, through the exploitation of the claims procedures. Architects will quickly know when such a contractor has been engaged when they get a letter saying: "Thank you for Architect's Instruction No. 1, which we have passed to our claims department"!

But whatever considerations are given to the effects of bad contract management and the resulting claims, on those involved in a particular contract, it is the overall effect on the national economy which is of the greatest concern. The following must be considered:

1. The cost of 'pricing the architect' referred to above, introduced by genuine contractors as a partial protection against anticipated losses, is estimated to range between 5% and 10% over all the industry.
2. Contractors have additional management costs resulting from having to employ extra staff in order to deal with multiple variations, and specialised staff and/or independent advisors to deal with the complexities of the claims procedures.
3. In order to remain solvent, the losses which contractors suffer as a result of inefficiency induced by others on a contract, or a group of concurrent contracts, have to be recovered on subsequent contracts.

These factors alone represent a very considerable non-productive on-cost to building contracting. But of even greater concern is the expense which follows when contractors are denied their true entitlement to compensation, and their claims are rejected by the building owner, resulting in a formal dispute situation.

The problems of time, inconvenience and cost, and the risks which face a contractor if he intends to pursue his claim by way of arbitration, are set out in detail in the opening paragraphs of Chapter 3 – Contractors. As explained, even if he is ultimately successful, he will not recover all that he is entitled to, and will not even recover all the expense to which he has been put. Sometimes he will be advised that it will cost him more to pursue a claim, than he could ever expect to recover from having done so.

Bearing in mind the increasingly stringent terms of modern building contracts, and the tough stand taken by all too many contractual officers, it is not surprising that there has been a steady increase in building disputation to the point where it can best be described as one of the few growth industries, as indicated by a leading member of the Judiciary:

It is my firm belief that arbitration has a very bright future indeed.[8]

All this has to be paid for, and is a total and massive loss to the national economy. It is also a drain, sometimes a disastrous drain, on the resources of those, particularly contractors and sub-contractors, who become embroiled in a formal dispute situation, often through no fault of their own.

The only people to benefit from such increasing disputation are the ever growing number of those engaged in the lucrative 'claims industry', like the author of this book – lawyers, claims consultants and experts of various kinds, who metaphorically sit like vultures in trees waiting to descend and feed on the rotting carcasses of contracts that have got out of control.

The majority of disputes are subject to arbitration and, as such, should be dealt with by a person with detailed knowledge of, and experience in, the subject matter of the dispute. Section 12.(1) of the Arbitration Act 1950 provides that the parties shall "submit to being examined by the arbitrator", indicating that the arbitrator may decide in what manner he will conduct the proceedings. But there followed a further intervention by the Courts in that it was held that, unless the parties were otherwise agreed, the arbitrator was bound to adopt the full-blown adversarial procedure as applicable to a trial in the High Court.[9] It is nevertheless thought that an arbitrator has a duty to suggest an alternative procedure, especially when, in his opinion, it would be appropriate and would result in a saving of time and expense.

Some of these problems may be overcome if Clause 41.9 of the Contract is not deleted. The arbitration will then be conducted in accordance with the "JCT Arbitration Rules" which would have the effect of reducing or eliminating unnecessary delay and expense.[10]

But intervention by the Courts was as nothing compared to the intervention by Parliament in enacting the Arbitration Act 1979, which can only be seen as a lawyers' charter. Prior to 1979, an arbitrator's award was final and binding on the parties. There could be no appeal to the Courts provided that the arbitrator had not misconducted himself or the proceedings, and provided that he had not given reasons for his decision. That he should not give reasons was advised by Lord Mansfield (1705–1793):

> Consider what you think justice requires and decide accordingly. But never give your reasons: for your judgment will probably be right but your reasons will certainly be wrong.[11]

And the same advice is given in a leading textbook, where it is said that an appeal may be made:

> ... where the award discloses an error upon its face. To avoid this latter possibility, awards are usually kept as short as possible and, if finality is desired, it is undesirable for an arbitrator to state his reasons for making his award.[12]

However, in enacting the 1979 Act, Parliament chose to contradict this wise advice by making it standard practice for arbitrators to give reasons for their awards, and by introducing a right to seek leave to appeal. The nonsense is best illustrated in JCT80 by Clause 41.5 which provides that the arbitrator's award "shall be final and binding on the parties", but by the immediately following Clause (41.6), the parties expressly agree that it should not be so!

It is the common case that a Respondent Employer will expect to be the loser and will have an interest in exploiting this right. He will therefore set his lawyers searching the arbitrator's reasons for the least possibility of finding grounds for seeking leave to appeal, no matter how tenuous. The purpose is to put the Claimant Contractor under such a financial strain that he will give up or, better still, be driven into bankruptcy or liquidation.

During the arbitration proceedings, the Claimant will have had to invest substantial sums of money in prosecuting his claim. Prior to 1979, the Claimant could expect to recover the amount awarded by the arbitrator, plus his costs, within a reasonable period of time. However, since 1979, if there is an appeal, none of these monies will be paid, and the Claimant will then have to provide further monies to finance his defence. This could cost upwards of £50,000 for a further period of a year or more. If the appeal is successful, and that could be on a mere legal technicality, the Claimant will have to pay the Respondent's costs and his own, and may well be faced with being sent back to square one, and having to start fresh arbitration proceedings before a new arbitrator.

However, the worst possible scenario is where, after a long period and a series of appeals, the Employer goes into liquidation, leaving the Contractor with no payment of the amount awarded by the arbitrator, no reimbursement of what has become a massive amount of costs and, the final straw, having to pay the arbitrator's costs. If nothing else encourages the avoidance of contractual disputes, this possibility most certainly should.

References

1 'The Placing and Management of Building Contracts'. Report of the Central Council for Works and Buildings, London; HMSO, 1944, Paragraph 20, page 9.

2 ibid, Paragraph 22, pages 9/10 – reproduced in Appendix 4 of this book.
3 ibid, 'Conclusions and Recommendations' I and II, page 28.
4 ibid, 'Conclusions and Recommendations' II, page 28.
5 ibid, Paragraph 18, page 8.
6 ibid, 'Conclusions and Recommendations' II, page 28.
7 Published paper: "The Contractor! Poor Devil!", Eric W. Seagrove FIOB FFB (Director, Y.J. Lovell (Holdings) Limited), 1973, the Faculty of Building.
8 "Arbitration in the Eighties", The Rt Hon. Lord Justice Donaldson, QC, March 1981. Paper given to, and published by, the Faculty of Building.
9 Per Mr Justice Donaldson in *The Myron* v *Tradax Export SA* [1969] 1 *Lloyd's Rep.* 411.
10 For a full explanation of the Rules, see *A User's Guide to the JCT Arbitration Rules*, Neil F. Jones, LLB(Hons), ACIArb, Oxford: BSP Professional Books, 1989.
11 Quoted in "The Law and Practice of Arbitrations", Dr John Parris LLB PhD, 1974, George Godwin Limited, at page 95.
12 *Hudson's Building and Engineering Contracts*, 10th Edition, London: Sweet & Maxwell, 1970, at page 868.

1
Architects

For the sake of brevity, all persons who act in a similar way to architects will be referred to as architects, whether they are in fact so qualified or not.

As first-call advisors to building owners, and subsequently as contract administrators, architects are in the very best position to prevent, or at least reduce, the incidence of claims in building contracts. Furthermore, if claims do nevertheless occur, they will, by virtue of their position as contract administrators, be placed in the best position to prevent them resulting in disputes and the possibility of legal proceedings.

In order to achieve this important objective, architects not only have to be efficient, they also have to be positive in all their dealings with others. When the parties execute the building contract, they appoint him specifically to make decisions – he should therefore do so, whether the parties like it or not – if they don't, they have the remedy of arbitration. Two examples will illustrate the point:

1. Suppose the contract requires the architect to form an opinion and make a decision – say, as to whether or not the contractor is entitled to an extension of time and loss and/or expense. The architect forms his opinion and publishes his decision to the contractor, who then protests.
2. The time has come for the architect to issue the Final Certificate, but he discovers that he cannot do so because the contractor and quantity surveyor are haggling over the final account. The architect should remind the quantity surveyor that Clause

30.6.1.2.2 of the Contract provides for him to issue the final account, and request that he do so forthwith. The architect should then issue the Final Certificate even though the contractor protests.

An architect should never allow arguments or haggling to develop – they waste a great deal of time and money. But far more importantly, to do so would suggest that he and/or the quantity surveyor are insecure as to their opinions, and that would increase the risk of the argument deteriorating into a dispute, and from that to arbitration. He should simply say, 'we have formed our opinions, and that is the end of the matter as far as we are concerned', and he should repeat this even if the contractor threatens arbitration.

The contractor's threat could be a bluff but, if it isn't, and he is properly advised, he will be warned that if the contractual officers can demonstrate that they have performed their contractual functions impartially and with care, it is most unlikely that an arbitrator would overturn their decisions. The architect and quantity surveyor will have done their best to avoid the occurrence of legal proceedings.

The exact opposite is illustrated by letters addressed to clients, which the author has seen, where the architect has said: "This matter has obviously got out of hand and will now have to be settled by arbitration". This is a gross dereliction of duty on his part because, by failing to make decisions, and sticking to them, the architect has made arbitration inevitable, and is directly responsible for what that implies.

Until a building contract is entered into, i.e. at Plan of Work Stage J, architects are first-call advisors and owe a duty exclusively to their clients, subject of course to their social, legal and professional responsibilities. It is an important part of their duty to protect their clients by advising them as to the procedures which will prevent, or at least reduce, the incidence of claims.

Architects should know that claims only occur when changes take place after the terms of the building contract have been agreed, and the Contractor appointed. Therefore, to prevent the occurrence of claims, there would have to be no such changes. However, because the Contract apportions the risks involved between the parties, some changes may occur which cannot be avoided. These are those which are caused by persons or agencies outside the control of the parties to the Contract, and are set out as Relevant Events in Clauses

25.4.1, 2, 3, 4, 7, 9, 10 and 11. Contractors' claims in respect of any of these matters will only be for extensions of time.

All other changes are within the control of the parties to the Contract, and are set out as Relevant Events in Clauses 25.4.5, 6, 8, 12, and 13. Contractors' claims in respect of these matters may be for extensions of time, but they will invariably also be for loss and/or expense under Clauses 26.1 and/or 34.3 of the Contract. Such claims can, and obviously should, be avoided.

The 'Simon' Report set out the principal reason for the occurrence of such changes and resulting claims:

> (a) Insufficient pre-contract preparation of the particulars of the work to be carried out.[1]

This message was underlined in the 'Conclusions and Recommendations' section:

> Inadequate pre-contract preparation is a major cause of inefficiency in the building industry. It makes it impossible for the general contractor to organise his work effectively; it is the cause of endless variations during the course of the work. The results are high costs and delays.[2]

For this state of affairs, and the results, the Report blamed the building owner for insisting on a rush job in the misguided belief that this would be in his best interests in the long run:

> Often he thinks that the obtaining of tenders is the only way by which he can satisfy himself as to cost and he presses the architect and quantity surveyor to get the contract fixed. The contract price in these circumstances contains a large number of provisional items which may prove to be quite unreliable; but this does not dissuade the building owner from entering into a contract as he often thinks that the sooner the work can be commenced upon the site the sooner the job will be finished.
>
> There can be no greater mistake. The result of a rushed job of this sort is that nobody has really thought out the details; the owner and the architect, neither of whom has had the opportunity of studying the plans in detail, frequently change their minds; all sorts of improvements, mistakes and difficulties are discovered as the job goes on. The architect is constantly forced to instruct the builder to make variations from the original contract, each one of which causes delay and extra cost, and gives rise to claims for additional payments by the builder.[3]
>
> The responsibility for this rush and inefficiency lies squarely on the shoulders of the building owner. He can prevent it if he wishes. He thinks that he is going to get a cheaper and quicker job by rush methods, but he is profoundly mistaken. The work will take longer and will cost more and he is the chief sufferer.[4]

This message was also underlined in the "Conclusions and Recommendations" section:

The building owner can prevent this. He should, with his architect do his thinking in advance and should see that the work is not started on the site until the whole job has been carefully thought out, and all requirements have been accurately defined in such detail as is necessary at this stage by drawings, specifications and bills of quantities.[5]

The Report also blamed:

1. Architects for failing to correct the building owner's misguided belief:

   When the owner wishes to insist on undue hurry, the architect should endeavour to convince him of the importance of having time to complete his designs in detail.[6]

2. The unnecessary use of Nominated Sub-Contractors:

   It is of the first importance that the general contractor should, subject to the directions of the architect, be in full control of the whole of the executive work on site. It is, therefore, desirable that as much of the work as possible should be fully described in the bills of quantities for the main contract, and should be priced and carried out by the general contractor or by firms selected by him, with whom he is accustomed to work and in whom he has confidence. This should ensure the best conditions for the success of his management of the whole contract.[7]

   The problems which are caused by the incorporation of Nominated Sub-Contractors are so well known that they should not need to be repeated. The following examples will suffice:

   (a) Forcing two quite separate companies to work together harmoniously is to ask a great deal, especially if they have not worked together previously, and the possibility of friction is even more likely if previous experience has left a lot to be desired.

   (b) If disputes arise between the Contractor and a Nominated Sub-Contractor, they will invariably blame each other, and the Architect will be placed in the difficult, if not impossible, position of having to decide which of them is at fault. If there are a number of Nominated Sub-Contractors, disputes are even more likely, and the Architect will definitely be put in an impossible position.

   (c) The difficulties for the Architect, and the financial consequences for the Employer, in the event of it becoming necessary to re-nominate during the course of the contract, are enormous, as will be appreciated from a careful study of Clause 35.24 of the Contract.

3. The failure of architects to make decisions as to Nominated Sub-Contractors before the Main Contract has been executed:

> Another result is that the contract is usually signed long before the details of the various sub-contracts have been settled, and indeed before the architect, who takes responsibility for selecting many of the sub-contractors, has even decided which firms he intends to nominate. The contractor, therefore, when he signs the contract, does not know when each sub-contractor will be ready to begin his job, what his needs will be or how long it will take him to finish. No reliable time and progress schedule can be made and no effective planning of the work is possible.[8]

The problems associated with Nominated Sub-Contractors are greatly increased if the nomination(s) is not made until after the Main Contract has been executed and work commenced on site:

(a) Either from previous experience, or from messages on the 'grapevine', the Contractor may not wish to accept the nomination, but cannot, for legal reasons, make a reasonable objection under Clause 35.5.1. Friction and disputes are virtually built-in from the start.

(b) The difficulties for the Architect, and the financial consequences for the Employer, in the event bf the Contractor being unable to agree the terms of NSC/T Part 3 with a Nominated Sub-Contractor can be very considerable. In this connection, architects would be well advised to consider the practical implications of Clauses 35.8.2 and 35.9.2, second alternative, of the recently amended Contract.

Where Nominated Sub-Contractors are truly unavoidable, the nominations should be decided upon before the Main Contract is executed, and the procedures recommended later should be followed most carefully.

The 'Simon' Report has been referred to, and its references to the importance of thorough pre-contract preparation have been repeated and emphasised in all subsequent reports on the subject of building contracts published by government and other agencies, and by, or with the approval of, the Royal Institute of British Architects (RIBA).[9-16] All these publications are bound to be brought to the attention of the Employer's legal advisors in the event of the Employer suffering damage due to a failure of the Architect to follow their recommendations and requirements.

It is also relevant to note that, on the basis of various comparative studies, it has long been known that productivity in the building industry in North America has always been considerably higher than in the United Kingdom, even after making allowances for differences in standards, climate, locality, fluctuating exchange rates, etc. These studies have been summarised in a BRE Current Paper[17] q.v., from which the following are extracts:

> Nevertheless, as a starting point, the mission found convincing evidence of higher productivity in US site operations – estimated at 50% better than in the UK – and of much quicker completions on projects. It attributed this better performance to several factors, but notably to: complete pre-planning of the job by building owner, architect and contractor; efficient co-ordination of contracting work; ... Thus, designers were exhorted to pre-plan effectively, to obtain a firm brief from the client, and to have all working drawings complete at tender stage; whilst contractors were advised to start work only when full information was available. ...[18]

> According to him, the 'lump sum' (fixed price) contract was still the most widely used in private work, and was obligatory for all public sector work. There was no bill of quantities, so that the owner and his consultants had to 'provide complete detailed plans and specifications describing methods, materials and standards'. Provisional sums and nominated sub-contractors were virtually unknown. Variations were costly and therefore rare – seldom exceeding 3% of contract value.[19]

> Nevertheless, his direct experience of operations of the Laing Property Company in the US and Canada convinced him that the UK industry was a very poor performer by comparison. In western Canada, for example, where wages were more than double those in the UK, and materials cost about 10% more, the Laing Company had recently completed a 1M ft^2 shopping development in a total of 17 months, from start to finish, at a cost of 50–60% of what it would have been in the UK, where it would have taken 5 years at least. Several other examples were quoted.[20]

> The shorter US construction times – ... – were illustrated by an in-depth 'paired' comparison of office buildings; construction took on average 83 weeks in the US as against 124 weeks in the UK. Put another way, the UK managed to construct only 158 gross m^2 of office space per week whilst in the US the total was 269 m^2.[21]

As the *Client's Guide* and *Working With Your Architect* were published by, or with the approval of, the RIBA, failure to have read them could never be used by an architect as a defence to an action for negligence at the suit of a client. Furthermore, bearing in mind the status of all these publications, and the qualifications of the members of the committees that produced them, an architect would find it impossible to engage an expert who would be able to persuade a judge to accept an opposite view.

An extract from the *Client's Guide* is annexed hereto as Appendix 6. However, the most important statement in this connection is that set out in *Working With Your Architect*, which an architect would ignore at his peril.

The author has heard it argued that thorough pre-contract preparation is an unattainable ideal. To accept such an argument would be to say that all the eminent authorities referred to above were unrealistic. In fact, the reason generally given in support of this argument is that building owners will not allow the preparation time which is necessary.

Be that as it may, an architect would be foolish if he did not explain to his client in detail the severe detriment which he would suffer from causing a contract to commence when there had been "insufficient pre-contract preparation of the particulars of the work to be carried out".[1] It should be pointed out to the client that not only will the work take longer and cost more, but also, due to the massive increase in administrative work which will be required post-contract:

1. The charges of all members of the design team will be considerably increased, and
2. The attention of all site supervisory staff will be distracted from the crucial task of detecting defects in the works. In a leading case, this was held to excuse an architect for failing to detect defects in the works:

> When he arrives on site there may be very many important matters with which he has to deal. ... It by no means follows that, in failing to discover a defect which a reasonable examination would have disclosed, in fact the architect was necessarily in breach of his duty to the building owner so as to be liable in an action for negligence.[22]

An architect would be even more foolish if he caused such a situation to arise through his own inefficiency or, as is often the case, because he wishes to:

> wait to see what the job looks like as it goes up and then change his mind or make new suggestions.[23]

Architects should take the following steps, at the various Plan of Work Stages, in order to protect their clients from the effects of claims, and to protect themselves against resulting actions for negligence.

A 'Inception'

On being approached by a prospective client, an architect should first consider whether or not the proposed commission should be accepted. If it is to be accepted:

1. The Architect should immediately take the Client's instructions and then prepare a preliminary design brief, in sufficient detail to enable him to consider how the work involved would fit in with his other commitments. He should then prepare, and give the Client, a preliminary programme for the project, setting out the various design stages, allowing sufficient time for thorough pre-contract preparation, and give the key date when it is anticipated that works could commence on site.

   If this step is not carried out, the Client may have a quite unrealistic idea as to when the building may be started, and it is then, when the design stages take longer than he anticipated, that he may well bring pressure on the Architect to speed up the process.

   It is appropriate to mention at this stage that it is common for projects to be divisible into sections, as, for example, a low-rise housing development, or a building consisting of separated blocks. In such a case, the Client may wish to occupy the sections as they are completed. The provisions of Clause 18, "Partial possession by Employer", should not be relied on, since the Employer has to obtain the consent of the Contractor before taking possession of any part, and the use of the Sectional Completion Supplement has considerable administrative disadvantages.

   In appropriate cases, the Architect should suggest to the Client that the project be divided into its parts, and each part treated as a separate contract. This method, sometimes referred to as 'parallel working', has considerable advantages, particularly in terms of programming, because it enables the first part to be proceeded with whilst the next part is being detailed. Furthermore, it provides valuable protection against the possibility of the Contractor not coming up to scratch, or getting into financial difficulties, and it encourages low tendering and good performance if the Contractor is told that, subject to his having given satisfaction, he will be invited to negotiate a tender for the second stage contract.

2. If the Client should object to the programme being too long, and brings pressure on the Architect to speed up the process, the Architect must explain to the Client the severe detriment which he would suffer from causing the building contract to commence without there having been thorough pre-contract preparation.

3. If the Architect cannot convince the Client that it would be in his best interests to allow sufficient time, he should seriously consider whether or not he should decline the commission. If he decides to accept, he should confirm his recommendations in writing, and couple that with a disclaimer of liability for all the consequences which will follow from the Client's requirements.

4. The Architect should explain the terms under which he would accept the commission, and agree the extent and limits of services to be provided, by reference to the RIBA 'Architect's Appointment'. In cases where the Client has pressed the Architect to proceed without thorough pre-contract preparation, the Architect should take into account the additional amount of post-contract administration, when setting the basis of his remuneration.

5. Once the contract with the Client has been agreed and executed, the Architect should:

   (a) Complete the design brief to cover all aspects of the Client's requirements, including project budget, statement of quality, etc.

   (b) Finalise the project programme, which should then be monitored regularly, and the Client kept informed of progress. If the programme has to be modified, as a result of unexpected developments, the reasons, and their effect, should be explained to the Client.

6. An architect should never attempt to deal with any matter on which he is not qualified and experienced. He may therefore require the assistance of Consultants for the next, and subsequent, Stages. For instance, for approximate estimates, sub-soil investigation, survey, mechanical services, etc.

   Architects should note that if, at any stage of a project, they wish to delegate any part of their design function to others, there are three courses open to them. These courses were set out by the Senior Official Referee in a case involving the design of a reinforced concrete portal frame:

One was to say: 'This is not my field'. The second was to go to the client, the building owner, and say:

> 'This reinforced concrete is out of my line. I would like you to employ a structural engineer to deal with this aspect of the matter'.

Or he can, while retaining responsibility for the design himself seek the advice and assistance of a structural engineer, paying for his service out of his own pocket but having at any rate the satisfaction of knowing that if he acts upon that advice and it turns out to be wrong, the person whom he employed to give the advice will owe the same duty to him as he, the architect, owes to the building owner.[24]

As regards this third course, architects should know that they are in no position to dictate contractual terms to their clients. And it must be said that any building owner, properly advised, would require the Architect to engage and be responsible for the work of anyone whom he requires to provide consultant design services. Prior to accepting such terms, an architect should consult his indemnity insurers.

In the same case, it was also said that:

> The architect has no power whatsoever to delegate his duty to anybody else, certainly not to a contractor* who would in fact have an interest which was entirely opposed to that of the building owner.[25]

However, architects should know that they would be entitled to delegate their decision making functions to Consultants or other specialists, **provided** that, before doing so, they had obtained the Client's express authority.[26]

7. If a Consultant(s) or other specialist(s) is to be engaged at this Stage, the Architect should ensure that he (they) can comply with the project programme and, if so, he should arrange an appropriate written contract, making sure to fix him (or them) with liability for the work involved.

8. The Architect should confirm the completed brief, project programme and, if appropriate, authority to engage a specialist(s), to the Client, and his written agreement should be obtained prior to proceeding to the next Stage.[27]

---

*This term would include not only specialist contractors, but also sub-contractors and suppliers.

B 'Feasibility'

1. On receipt of the Client's permission to proceed, the Architect should consider, by reference to the RIBA *Architect's Job Book*, the matters which are likely to affect the feasibility of the particular project, bearing in mind that the necessary investigations vary from project to project.
2. The Architect should then, in collaboration with such specialist(s) as are to be engaged, carry out the necessary investigations and, when completed, provide a written report to the Client.
3. The feasibility investigations may reveal a problem(s) in the implementation of the brief. In such cases the Architect should advise the Client as to the possible courses of action which might be taken to overcome the problem(s). If the decision is to modify the brief, the Architect should prepare a revised brief including, if necessary, a revised project programme.
4. The revised brief should be submitted to the Client and his written authority should be obtained prior to proceeding to the next Stage.[28]

C 'Outline Proposals'

As architects should know, the 'Plan of work for design team operation' (PoW) was originally published in 1964 in the first edition of the RIBA *Handbook of Architectural Practice and Management*, but is now published separately.

Its purpose is defined in the Introduction as "a systematic plan of work for the design team" and a "model procedure for methodical working of the design team". Since its original publication, the PoW has been widely accepted by all those involved with building procurement.

The PoW sets out the various stages through which a conventional building project passes from inception to completion, with explanations as to the functions to be performed at all these stages by those directly involved. As architects should also know, the functions to be performed by them are enlarged in the RIBA *Architect's Job Book*, by reference to which an architect's performance will be judged.

Most importantly the PoW broke down the previously accepted stages, referred to in the 'Outline PoW' (Appendix 5), as the 'Usual

Terminology', into smaller stages. The reason for this was to ensure that as little as possible abortive work resulted from proceeding with unnecessary detail until each stage had been completed and approved by the building owner. This is of particular importance to the design stages, of which 'Outline Proposals' is the first of two.

The form which 'Outline Proposals' may take will vary with the type of project and, with a complex project, the Stage may consist of a series of development studies. Because this will be the first presentation of the Architect's interpretation of the Client's brief, it is likely that alterations may be required. The Architect should explain to his Client that because the design team has a great deal of work to do in the next Stage, in order to provide a fully developed design, the Employer should give the 'Outline Proposals' very careful consideration, and that he should not hesitate to withhold his approval until he is completely satisfied.

When the Client is satisfied with the 'Outline Proposals', the Architect should obtain "an approximation of the construction cost"[29] and submit this to the Client. When the Client has finally agreed the 'Outline Proposals' and approximate estimate, the Architect should provide the Client with an up-to-date version, and his written authority should be obtained prior to proceeding to the next Stage.[30]

On receipt of the Client's authority to proceed to the next Stage, the Architect should provide copies of the 'Outline Proposals' to such specialists as are to be appointed, in order that they clearly understand what is then proposed and what is expected of them.

D 'Scheme Design'

This represents the final design stage in which input is required by the Client. As indicated in the 'Outline PoW' (Appendix 5), the work now to be carried out by the design team is:

> To complete the brief and decide on particular proposals, including planning arrangement, appearance, structural method, outline specification, and cost, and to obtain all approvals.

The importance and significance of the Client's approval of the 'Scheme Design' cannot be over-emphasised, as is explained in the *Client's Guide* (Appendix 6), and architects should take particular note of the following:

It is clearly vital that before the client gives approval he is not merely satisfied with the scheme design but fully understands it.

Although a request for an alternative scheme design is bound to cost time and money, the cost of any alteration to the scheme design at this stage will still be small compared with that of making changes later.[31]

Approval of the final scheme design marks the watershed of the design phase. Every requirement should have been worked out within the cost plan and agreed by all concerned, and it is normally unwise and certainly expensive to alter the design after this. About half of the design team's work goes into the following stage – the translation of the scheme design into working drawings and specification notes which between them exactly describe every detail of the building's construction – and much of this work will have to be done again from the beginning if any change is made in the scheme design after it has been approved.[32]

Architects should also take particular note of what is expected of them at this Stage by the RIBA:

The architect will already have satisfied himself that the preliminary design solves all the client's problems and is technically satisfactory. But the design has now to be worked out in the minutest detail, by the designers by a continuous process of interchanging ideas and investigating alternatives for cladding materials, finishes, service installations and many other things. When every detail has been worked out within the cost plan, and agreed by all concerned, the design should be 'frozen', and not altered thereafter.[33]

An identical message is given in a government publication (Appendix 7) addressed to all building owners,[34] and in a leaflet published by the RIBA, and specifically addressed to building owners where it is said that:

A change of mind by client or architect that can be effected with a rubber and pencil at this stage may be infinitely more difficult and costly twelve months later.[35]

Whilst preparing the 'Scheme Design' the Architect will need to work closely with such specialist(s) as have been appointed, and with the Quantity Surveyor as regards the cost implications of the developing design. The Architect should consult with the Client if any deviation from the approved 'Outline Proposals' is necessary or desirable, and he should draw attention to the significance of the warning given at the end of the 'Scheme Design' Stage in the 'Outline PoW' (Appendix 5):

Brief should not be modified after this point.

Bearing in mind the costs involved, the Architect should be particularly careful to obtain the Client's written authority prior to proceeding to the next Stage.[36]

E 'Detail Design'

There will be no need for the Client to be involved in this Stage, unless some unexpected technical difficulty is discovered which entails an amendment to the 'Scheme Design' and/or the cost plan. If such a situation should arise, the Architect should immediately contact the Client and explain the circumstances and its implications in terms of cost and programme, and proceed no further until he has obtained the Client's express authority to the changes.

As will be seen from the 'Outline PoW' (Appendix 5), prior to its publication this, and the subsequent Stages F 'Production Information', G 'Bills of Quantities' had been referred to as 'Working Drawings'. This arrangement was most unsatisfactory, since it failed to recognise that two quite distinct functions are involved:

1. Technical decision making.
2. The production of the documents which will be required by Contractors, Sub-Contractors and Suppliers.

Where these functions were allowed to overlap, it was quite common for it to be necessary to carry out alterations to construction drawings and/or specifications as new decisions came to be made, leading to delay and abortive costs.

As the 'Outline PoW' (Appendix 5) stipulates, during the 'Detail Design' Stage, and prior to starting on the subsequent Stages, it is the design team's duty:

> To obtain final decisions on every matter related to design, specification, construction and cost.

A building owner, properly advised, will know that the reason for sticking strictly to this regime is emphasised by the warning in the 'Outline PoW' (Appendix 5) which follows Stage E 'Detail Design':

> Any further change in location, size, shape, or cost after this time will result in abortive work.

The Client, properly advised, will therefore require the Architect to confirm that this duty has been fulfilled, prior to authorising him to proceed to the following Stages. Accordingly, as the Client's first-call advisor and leader of the design team, it is the Architect's duty to ensure that no design decisions are postponed by the inclusion in the Bills of Quantities of provisional measurements (other than those relating to ground works), Provisional or Prime Cost Sums, or by producing outline rather than detailed drawings and specifications.

The following is a list of steps which should be taken in order to achieve this objective:

1. The Quantity Surveyor should provide a detailed cost plan to each member of the design team.
2. The approved Scheme Design should be developed by the Architect in consultation with Consultant(s), all decisions being monitored against cost plan.
3. Nominated Sub-Contractors are to be used only where wholly unavoidable, and only in respect of which the Architect has obtained the Client's express authority as required by NSC/T Part 1, and where the Client has executed the Employer/ Nominated Sub-Contractor Agreement NSC/W.
4. Nominated Suppliers are to be used only where wholly unavoidable, and only in respect of which the Architect has obtained the Client's express authority and where the Client has executed the Warranty TNS/2s.
5. In cases where Sub-Contractors and/or Suppliers are to provide design information, this should be obtained at this Stage for incorporation in the overall design.
6. The Architect should obtain the Client's express approval prior to the incorporation of any short-life materials; innovative design; unconventional products or systems; etc.
7. The Architect should exercise special care where detail and/or specification modifications to any part of the building are made necessary as a result of his design co-ordination function.
8. All design and specification decisions should be double-checked by members of the design team with British Standards and Codes of Practice, BRE Digests, manufacturers' and trade association recommendations, as appropriate.
9. Members of the design team should send details to, and obtain approval from, all manufacturers of proprietory products and/ or systems which are to be incorporated in the project.
10. The Architect should obtain specialist advice, or a second opinion, where any doubt exists as to the satisfactory nature of any part of the design or specification details.
11. The Architect must set up and operate rigorous checking procedures, and ensure that other members of the design team do likewise.

Finally, having ensured that design information from all sources is complete and integrated, the Architect should provide the Client with written confirmation, signed by all members of the design team, that the requirements of the 'Detail Design' Stage have been fully met, and that no design decisions remain to be taken. The Architect should then obtain the Client's written authority to instruct the design team to proceed to the next Stage[37]

F 'Production Information'

1. The Architect should instruct all other members of the design team to prepare their production information, and to submit this to him.
2. Where Nominated Sub-Contractors and Suppliers are to be used, the Architect should obtain tenders at this Stage, if they have not been previously obtained, and make his selections, so that the following matters may be considered in good time:

   (a) NSC/T Part 2, page 6 will show the prospective Nominated Sub-Contractor's programme. These should be compared with the anticipated main contract programme. Such a comparison may reveal that acceptance of a prospective Nominated Sub-Contractor would entail a delay in the main contract programme, with an inevitable contract over-run.

   (b) Section 6 of Schedule 2 of each Tender TNS/1 will show the prospective Nominated Supplier's programme and delivery periods. These should also be compared with the anticipated main contract programme. Such a comparison may reveal that acceptance of a prospective Nominated Supplier would entail a delay in the main contract programme, with an inevitable contract over-run.

   (c) If either of these situations was not discovered until after the Contractor had been appointed, the consequences would be very serious:

      (i)   In the case of Nominated Sub-Contractors, no agreement could be reached in respect of NSC/T Part 2, Item 1, for annexation to NSC/A; the Contractor would operate Clause 35.8.2 of the Contract; the Architect's only option would be to operate Clause 35.9.2; delay and disruption would occur and the Contractor would be entitled to extensions of time and loss and/or expense.

(ii) In the case of Nominated Suppliers, the Architect would discover that he was not entitled to make the nomination, by virtue of Clause 36.4, because a contract of sale could not be entered into due to the Contractor being able to satisfy the Supplier as regards delivery periods (Clause 36.4.3 of the Contract). If the Architect was unable to find an alternative Supplier, he would have no alternative but to agree with the Contractor accepting the nomination on terms that he would be automatically entitled to extensions of time and loss and/or expense.

(iii) If the programmes of other Nominated Sub-Contractors and/or Suppliers were affected, the complications regarding extensions of time and loss and/or expense would be very considerable indeed.

(d) It should be patently obvious to the Architect that the practical and financial consequences for his Client of either of these situations not being discovered until after the Contractor had been appointed would be very severe indeed. It is therefore the Architect's duty to advise his Client as to how these situations can be avoided, by adopting the following options, either individually or in combination:

(i) To pre-order goods and/or services.

In the case of Nominated Sub-Contractors, the Architect should ask to be supplied with details of the lead-in time. Armed with this information, the Architect can advise as to the amount of preparation work it would be necessary to pre-order so as to avoid the problem. This is envisaged by Clause 2.2. of the Employer/Nominated Sub-Contractor Agreement NSC/W.

In the case of Nominated Suppliers the Architect can advise as to the amount of such pre-ordering as would be necessary in order to avoid the problem.

(ii) To postpone the Date of Possession.

The effect on the contract programme of either of these situations not being discovered until after the Contractor had been appointed is illustrated in lines 1 and 2 of the diagram annexed hereto as Appendix 2, and the two opinions are illustrated in lines 3 and 4.

The financial consequences for the client of either of these situations not being discovered until after the Contractor had been appointed, compared with the result of adopting one or other of the options, are illustrated in a simplified example annexed hereto as Appendix 3.

3. Another reason why the Architect should obtain tenders from Nominated Sub-Contractors and Suppliers and make his selections, during this Stage, is so that the Quantity Surveyor can include appropriate Provisional Sums and full details of any associated 'builder's work' in the Bills of Quantities.
4. The Architect should make a final check of all production information in satisfaction of his duty to co-ordinate and integrate into the overall design the services provided by specialist(s).[38]
5. The Architect should, during this Stage, keep the Quantity Surveyor informed as to progress, and the date when the documents will be submitted for the preparation of the Bills of Quantities. This will enable the Quantity Surveyor to organise his work so as to avoid a delay in the pre-contract period.
6. Finally, the Architect should confirm to the Client that this Stage has been completed, and should seek his written authority to instruct the Quantity Surveyor to proceed to the next Stage.[39]

G 'Bills of Quantities'

1. The Architect should send a complete set of production information to the Quantity Surveyor.
2. The Quantity Surveyor should be instructed that, under no circumstances whatsoever:

   (a) Is the quality of any materials or the standards of workmanship to be described as a matter for the opinion of the Architect.[40]
   (b) Is the term "equal or other approved" to be used in relation to any materials or goods.
   (c) Are Provisional Sums or provisional measurements to be included without the express permission of the Architect.

3. The Quantity Surveyor's role at this Stage is of crucial importance. If there is anything which he does not understand, it is

likely that the Bills of Quantities would not properly represent the works, and this would create problems, and disputes, during the carrying out of work on site. The Architect should therefore make it clear to the Quantity Surveyor that if he is in any doubt on any matter, or if he should discover any aspect of the work which has not been fully detailed or specified, he is to notify the Architect immediately.

4. If the Quantity Surveyor should raise queries, these should be dealt with immediately, and the Architect should ensure that:

   (a) Such queries should be provided by list, but if they are raised at meetings or on the telephone, they should be reduced to writing and confirmed. In this, as in all situations involving others, the Architect must always avoid the possibility of a 'falling between stools', as happened in a 1974 case where an architect and a quantity surveyor were involved.[41]

   (b) Any further drawings, details or specifications which result are incorporated in the set of production information.

   (c) Existing drawings, details or specifications are amended as necessary.

5. In conjunction with the Quantity Surveyor, the Architect should:

   (a) Ensure that there are no discrepancies in or divergences between the production information and the Bills of Quantities.

   (b) Correctly set out the details as to how the form of contract will be completed. In this connection it is very bad practice for the names of practices to be entered in Articles 3 (A or B) and 4. By the use of the singular in both cases, the Contract clearly envisages that the names of particular persons will be entered. And it should be obvious that, as a matter of law, only named persons can perform the duties entrusted to these contractual officers.

   In Chapter 3 – Contractors, the technique of 'pricing the architect' will be explained. If the names of practices are entered, this pricing will be related to the member of that practice that the tenderers judge to have the worst "reputation for efficiency and fair play".

   It is clearly in the interests of all, and particularly those of the Employer, that the names of the particular persons who will in practice perform the duties entrusted to these officers should be entered in Articles 3 (A or B) and 4.

(c) Carefully consider the Contractors who will be recommended to the Client for including in the tender list. A check should be made to ensure that all prospective tenderers have a good past record, have efficient quality control staff and procedures, and are prepared to provide an indemnity to the Architect and Consultants in respect of defective materials and/or workmanship.

(d) Make suggestions to and consult with the Client as to the rate of "Damages for non-completion" under Clause 24.2.1 of the Contract.

6. Finally, the Architect should:

(a) Confirm to the Client that this Stage has been completed, and should seek his written authority to obtain tenders.[42]

(b) Submit the proposed tender list to the Client for his approval.

(c) Exercise special vetting of any tenderers which the Client may ask to be included on the tender list, recommending their exclusion if justified. If the Client should insist on the inclusion of any tenderers against whom either the Architect or Quantity Surveyor have raised objection, a written disclaimer of liability should be issued.

H 'Tender Action'

The Architect should follow the requirements of the NJCC Code of Procedure, and should ensure that the Quantity Surveyor does likewise. Having carried out the checks required by Section 6 of the Code, the Quantity Surveyor should report his findings and recommendations to the Architect.

Architects should appreciate that no matter how carefully they have proceeded up to this point, major problems could still occur after the Contractor has been appointed. Therefore, the Architect should take the following steps prior to making a recommendation to the Client for the acceptance of a tender:

1. Obtain confirmation in writing from:

(a) All prospective Nominated Sub-Contractors and Suppliers that they have no objection to the prospective Contractor.

(b) The prospective Contractor that he has no objection to the nomination of any of the prospective Nominated Sub-Contractors or Suppliers.

The Architect should consult with the Quantity Surveyor, and the relevant Consultant if appropriate, if any objections are made which he considers to be reasonable, in order to decide whether there should be a change of prospective Nominated Sub-Contractor(s) or Supplier(s), or alternatively of the prospective Contractor.

Solving this particular problem will be made more difficult if pre-ordering of goods and services has been involved.

2. If the confirmations are provided, the Architect should pass:

(a) All NSC/T Part 2s to the prospective Contractor, and call on him to consult with all prospective Nominated Sub-Contractors, and to confirm in writing that he would be able to agree an integrated programme.

(b) All TNS/1s to the prospective Contractor, and call on him to consult with the prospective Nominated Suppliers, and to confirm in writing that he will be able to obtain the relevant materials or goods from all prospective Nominated Suppliers to suit his programme requirements.

3. If the prospective Contractor cannot confirm that he is able to agree an integrated programme with all prospective Nominated Sub-Contractors, and/or that he will be able to obtain the relevant materials or goods from all prospective Nominated Suppliers to suit his programme requirements, the prospective Contractor should be asked to explain the difficulty.

The Architect should then consult with the Quantity Surveyor, and the relevant Consultant if appropriate, in order to consider and investigate whether or not the difficulty could be overcome by a change of the prospective Nominated Sub-Contractor(s) or Supplier(s), or alternatively of the prospective Contractor.

4. If it is decided that the difficulty would not be overcome by making any such changes, the Architect should advise the Client that he should agree to the Date of Possession being postponed.

5. All members of the design team should do a final check before recommending acceptance of a tender, and seeking the Client's written authority to prepare the Contract Documents for execution.

6. The Client should be reminded that up to this point, the Architect's and the Quantity Surveyor's sole responsibilities have been to him, but that this will no longer be the case once the Contract is executed, if the Architect and the Quantity Surveyor are to be appointed under Articles 3 (A or B) and 4. From that point on, whilst still having responsibilities to him, they will both have legal and professional duties to act independently and impartially as between the Employer and the Contractor in a number of respects.

7. Because the difficulties for the Client in the event of a contractor becoming bankrupt, or going into liquidation, during the course of a contract are enormous, the Architect should recommend the Client to instruct his accountants to investigate and provide him with a report as to the financial standing of the prospective Contractor.

8. The Architect should obtain the following from the prospective Contractor:

   (a) His evidence of insurances, and he should forward the documents to the Client for the consideration of his insurance brokers or solicitors.

   (b) His proposed Master Programme. Provision of the Master Programme before execution of the Contract is envisaged by Clause 5.3.1.2 of the Contract. It is desirable that this be obtained at this Stage, because it may reveal difficulties for the Client and/or members of the design team and, whilst a prospective Contractor can be called upon to amend his programme pre-contract, he cannot be required to do so after execution of the Contract.

   The Architect should insist on the Master Programme being presented in network form with the critical path clearly shown. Only in this form will the Architect be able to assess the effects of any delays which may be notified by the Contractor.

   (c) The dates, in schedule form and also marked on the Master Programme, on which the Contractor will require instructions in regard to any information that may be outstanding. In this regard, there are four very important matters of which the Architect should take note:

   (i) Strictly speaking, the Contractor is under no obligation to ask for outstanding information. Under Clause 5.4 of the Contract, it is the Architect's duty to provide outstanding information whether or not the Contractor makes application.

(ii) Nevertheless, if the Contractor knows of further information which he will require, his failure to apply for that information at the appropriate time can be taken into account by the Architect in respect of any notice under Clauses 25.2 and 25.4.6, and/or any application under Clauses 26.1 and 26.2.1, that he may receive from the Contractor.

However, circumstances may occur in which a contractor will not know of the need for additional information until he actually comes to the relevant piece of construction.

(iii) There will be circumstances in which the Contractor will not know when he requires certain information. The most common case is where there is a P.C. (Prime Cost) Sum for goods or materials. With the best will in the world, the Contractor will have no way of knowing the delivery periods which will apply to the actual goods or materials which he will ultimately be instructed to order.

In respect of such matters the dates given by the Contractor will be no more than 'guesstimates', which he cannot be held to. The Architect must, therefore, in order to avoid having to grant extensions of time and loss and/or expense, make his selections and establish delivery times as early as possible, in order to be able to issue instructions in good time.

(iv) A contractor may know of information which he will require, but genuinely believes that this will be forthcoming from the Architect without his need to apply for it. But the Architect, equally genuinely, thinks that he has provided all outstanding information.

This unfortunate 'falling between stools' can all too easily lead to disputes. The Architect can avoid this by writing to the Contractor, when providing what he believes is the last of the outstanding information, to state that fact. The Contractor is then on notice that if there is anything further which he requires he must apply for it.

9. Obtain confirmation from the Client that there will be no difficulty in his handing over the site to the Contractor on or before the Date of Possession.
10. Ask the Quantity Surveyor to prepare a cash-flow projection to provide the client with forewarning of the likely value of Interim Certificates.

J 'Project Planning'

The Architect should:

1. Prepare the Contract Documents and ensure, in everyone's interest, that these are executed by both parties prior to work commencing on site.
2. Brief the site supervisory team, reminding those to be responsible for carrying out inspections of work on site that they are required to:

   (a) Operate by using predictive techniques and checklists, and that they must ensure that no vital construction is covered up until after it has been inspected and found satisfactory. If any construction is found to be unsatisfactory, it is not to be covered up until after it has been re-inspected and found satisfactory.

   (b) Notify the Architect immediately should any dispute arise as to the quality of materials, goods or workmanship. It is the Architect's duty to inspect personally the work involved, because only he has the power to condemn anything which is not in accordance with the Contract. In making his decision in such circumstances, the Architect must act with complete impartiality.

   (c) Provide weekly reports dealing with the works inspected; the progress achieved by comparison with the Contractor's Master Programme; any difficulties which may be foreseen; etc.

3. Remind the Clerk of Works that his powers are limited to issuing Directions, and that the Contractor is not obliged to act on such Directions until they are confirmed in writing by the Architect. He should also be reminded of his duties and the requirements for weekly reports.[43]

4. Advise the client that he should:

   (a) Hand over the site on or before the Date for Possession.
   (b) Not interfere in any way with the Contractor or the works.
   (c) Not make any visits to the site unless accompanied by the Architect or one of his representatives.
   (d) Make prompt payment on Interim Certificates.

5. Issue to the Contractor:

   (a) All documents referred to in Clauses 5.2 and 5.3.1.1 of the Contract.
   (b) Instructions regarding Nominated Sub-Contractors and Suppliers, if any.

6. Conduct first project meeting.
7. Remind Consultants:

   (a) Of their areas of responsibility for inspections of work on site, and the requirement for them to provide reports following each inspection.
   (b) That they must not issue any instructions to the Contractor or any Sub-Contractor, except in an emergency situation.
   (c) That details of any instructions which they wish to issue must be provided to the Architect, because it is only he, the Architect, who has power to issue instructions, and because he is obliged to seek the Employer's authority prior to issuing variation instructions.

8. Remind the Contractor that he must not act on any instructions from anyone until they have been confirmed in writing by the Architect, except in an emergency situation.
9. Notify all manufacturers or suppliers of specified materials, products and systems, so as to ensure that problems are not caused by delayed ordering or the use by the Contractor of substitute materials.

K 'Operations on Site'

The following matters are of special importance during this Stage:

1. If any production information is outstanding:

   (a) From the Architect: he should plan to ensure that this is issued as soon as possible, but certainly well before the dates required by the Contractor's Master Programme agreed earlier.

(b) From Consultant(s): the Architect should monitor the Contractor's Master Programme regarding the latest dates by which that information should be provided to him and to the Contractor, and remind the Consultant(s) in good time.

2. Any problems which may arise should be dealt with promptly and efficiently.

3. As first-call advisor to the Client, and as leader of the design team, the Architect has a duty to monitor the work of:

   (a) The Quantity Surveyor to ensure that all valuations are carried out correctly and, most importantly, at the proper time, so that he, the Architect, can comply with the requirements of Clauses 3 and 30 of the Contract.

   (b) Any Consultants, to ensure that they are being meticulous in carrying out inspection of the works for which they are responsible.

   (c) The site supervisory team, and Clerks of Works if any, to ensure that they are also being meticulous in the carrying out of their inspection duties.

4. The Architect should obtain a Financial Statement from the Quantity Surveyor,[44] and incorporate this into a general monthly report to the Client.[45]

5. There are commonly occurring situations which the Architect should always avoid:

   (a) Giving approvals of any kind except in respect of the following matters:

      (i) Aesthetic, such as the appearance, but only the appearance of, sample brickwork panels.

      (ii) Where truly unavoidable, such as inspections of exposed formations prior to the casting of foundations. However, except in the simplest of cases, the Architect would be wise to delegate this task to a consultant engineer, even if he had to pay the engineer himself!

   Except in such matters, the Contract does not require the Architect to give approvals, and he should avoid providing a quality control service for the Contractor for which he will not be paid. Furthermore, there is great danger for the

Architect if, at a later stage, the approved materials, goods or workmanship should prove to be defective, especially if covered up and difficult to remedy.

The Architect should instruct the site supervisory team, and Clerks of Works if any, that they must also avoid giving approvals.

(b) Acting out of sympathy if the Contractor is in difficulty, unless he has first obtained the Client's written authority. Sir Hugh Casson is reported as having once said that: "If you scratch an architect, what you will find is a boy scout with a power complex". Architects should avoid their boy scout tendencies.

(c) Accepting any 'botched' solutions or inadequate materials which the Contractor may suggest if supply or other difficulties occur. If for any reason the Client should insist on such acceptance, the Architect should issue a written disclaimer of liability for the consequences.

The Architect should remember that he only has an obligation to require the removal of defective materials, goods or works, and no authority to order replacements, except in regard to any products which are no longer attainable.

(d) Conducting regular site meetings. The author has been unable to find anyone who remembers this practice being followed prior to 1966. It is suggested that the reason for the practice having become such a common occurrence since then, is that a fundamental misunderstanding existed in the mind of whoever wrote the section on meetings in a handbook which was first published in 1965.[46] In that section various types of meetings were described, including:

> 3. Co-ordination meetings
> These include project meetings, site meetings, and all others primarily concerned with the progress and control of the job. . . . Their purpose is to assess the situation, to determine critical factors, to formulate a brief for action, to co-ordinate, and to delegate responsibility for action.[47]

The Plan of Work was included in the Handbook. Under Col.2 the duties of the Architect included the requirement that he should:

Hold regular site meetings.[48]

It was therefore suggested that architects should take control of the job. That was very bad advice indeed, because it could expose architects to criminal and civil legal consequences, which their indemnity insurance would be unlikely to cover. It is the Contractor's duty and responsibility to control the job, and the Architect should not usurp his authority or relieve him of that responsibility.

If the Contractor should choose to conduct regular co-ordination meetings, the Architect should only attend if he is invited, and only then as an observer.

There are other reasons why the Architect should never conduct regular site meetings:

(i)   Unless special arrangements have been made, the Architect will have no authority to conduct meetings on the site without the Contractor's permission. Furthermore, it involves departures from the procedures expressly author-ised by the Client.

(ii) Unless the Architect has allowed for the additional time which he will spend in conducting such meetings, preparing agendas, "minutes", etc., when agreeing with the Client as to his remuneration, either his profit will be seriously reduced or he will have to neglect his primary duty, which is to 'look sharply after the builder'.

(iii) Considering the number of people which are expected to attend, and bearing in mind the number of on-going contracts at any one time, the overall cost of such meetings adds an enormous non-productive on-cost to the total budget for building. The cost implications of regular monthly site meetings were dealt with in the concluding paragraphs of an article entitled "Site meetings: are they necessary?", in *The Architect's Journal*:[49]

> If on average, five people are involved at each site meeting and the total time is four hours, then the cost per meeting could be something like £250. This can be doubled if the productivity lost by attending is taken into account, so giving £500 per meeting. With an average contract running over 18 months, the cost of monthly site meetings per contract may be close on £9000.
>
> It is anyone's guess how many contracts are in progress throughout the UK at any one time, but on the basis of the above figures, the industry is loading itself with a cost of £9 000 000 for every 1000 contracts. The mind boggles at the thought of there being perhaps 5555 contracts costing £50 000 000 in site meetings.

As the RPI has doubled since 1981, when this article was written, all the above figures would need to be doubled for 1993.

(iv) The *Architect's Job Book* made the assumption that the Architect would chair regular site meetings. The amount of work caused to all concerned may be judged from Section 1 "Architect's **progress** meetings (policy)".[50] And one only has to look at the proposed agenda for these meetings,[51] to appreciate that every item is either unnecessary and could be far better done by methods other than at meetings; or, of greatest importance, should never be raised at a meeting at all:

The heading itself is very revealing: "Architect's **progress** meetings: Agenda". The Architect does not require a meeting to consider progress. As has been explained in Section J.2.c, the site supervisory staff, and Clerk of Works if any, will be monitoring, and providing weekly reports on, progress.

1: Agree minutes of last meeting.

This would not occur if there had not been a previous site meeting. In any case the term "minutes" is only appropriate for a committee meeting which, bearing in mind the various individuals, firms and companies attending, a site meeting cannot be.

2: Contractor's report.
3: Clerk of works' report.
4: Consultants' reports.
5: Quantity surveyor's report.

Any reports which the Architect may require should be in writing, and supplied at the intervals which he decrees. Verbal reports, delivered at a meeting, as is implied, should never ever be permitted.

6: Communications and procedures.

What this means is not understood. All such matters should have been settled and established at the Initial (pre-contract) Meeting.

7: Contract completion date.

This is quite unacceptable. The Client has agreed to the Contract, Clause 25 of which provides very specific rules for the Contractor and the Architect to follow in respect of delays and any amendments which may be made to the Completion Date. The Architect should never allow the Contractor to by-pass these rules. The Contractor will not deal with matters, such as delays, in accordance with the provisions of the Contract, as he is required to do, but will wait for the next site meeting, knowing that the Architect is one of those who is quite prepared to "sort things out on the site".

8: Any other business.

This item should never be allowed in any case because it provides the Contractor, and possibly others, with an open invitation to introduce a 'hidden agenda', with all the problems that that would cause for the Architect.

9: Date, time and place of next site meeting.

This would not be necessary if there was not going to be a next site meeting.

(v) When disputes arise, the so-called 'minutes', which are in many cases far from being what they should be, provide marvellous material for endless happy and expensive hours of contrary interpretation and argument for the parties' advocates.

The only possible justification for regular site meetings, chaired by the Architect, is when there has been inadequate pre-contract preparation; various provisional measurements and Provisional and Prime Cost Sums have been included in the Bills of Quantities; a number of Sub-Contractors and Suppliers have been nominated after work has started; and when there are numerous variations. Under such circumstances, it is quite impossible for the Contractor to manage the works, and there is no alternative but for the Architect to call and conduct regular site meetings in order to sort out the recurrent resulting chaos – what may be described as a 'damage limitation exercise'!

This is not to say that the Architect should never conduct site meetings, of course not. Even with a thoroughly prepared contract, unexpected situations can arise. It is then that a site meeting might be helpful. When such a necessity arises, the Architect should follow the recommendations set out in the Handbook under the marginal heading "Requirements for a meeting".[52]

6. Extensions of time:

(a) If the Architect should receive Clause 25.2.1.1 notices, he should deal with these promptly, and strictly in accordance with Contract conditions, i.e. within 12 weeks (Clause 25.3.1). If a notice is deficient of the necessary information required by Clause 25.2, the Architect should immediately inform the Contractor that until that information is provided, he cannot perform his duties under Clause 25.3.

(b) In a recent case[53] it has been held that an architect may, in certain circumstances, be under a duty to grant an extension of time despite not having received notice of delay from the Contractor:

> It is pointed out in a passage from *Keating* on *Building Contracts* (4th Edn)[54] at p346, which is cited by the arbitrator, that if the architect wrongly assumes that a notice is a condition precedent to the performance of the duty of the architect to form an opinion and take appropriate steps:
>
> > "and in consequence refuses to perform such duties the employer loses his right to liquidated damages. It may therefore be against the employer's interests for an architect not to consider a cause of delay of which late notice is given or of which he has knowledge despite lack of notice."

Following this extract, the learned author went on to offer the following advice to architects:

> In the latter case it is suggested that frequently the better course for the architect is to invite notice. When it is received, or, if not received within a reasonable time, at the expiration of that time he should consider the matter and grant any appropriate extension.

(c) The Architect must of course grant an extension if he decides that it is justified. However, this will automatically mean that hand-over of the building will be late, and that could have serious consequences for the Client. Therefore, before issuing the extension of time, the Architect should ask the Contractor at what price he would be able to accelerate the work so as to bring the project back on course. The Architect can then give the Client the option of paying the extra, in order to get his building on time. If the Client accepts this option, the agreement can be put in formal terms by the parties' legal advisors.

7. Loss and/or expense:
   If the Architect should receive Clause 26.1 applications, he should also deal with these promptly and strictly in accordance with Contract conditions. The Architect should note that the Contractor does not have to give any details when making an application. Therefore, if the Architect should require further details, he should immediately operate the provisions of Clause 26.1.2 of the Contract.

   If the Architect should be of the opinion that the Contractor's application is justified, he should exercise the right conferred on him by Clause 26.1 to instruct the Quantity Surveyor to ascertain the amount of the loss and/or expense. Such communications should, like all those between the Architect and others, be confirmed in writing.

8. Because they are not always appreciated, there are matters regarding extensions of time and loss and/or expense which must be explained:

   (a) The development of lump-sum contracts and related procedures has been increasingly to circumscribe and limit the Contractor's risks. This has been for the benefit of the Employer because it has removed uncertainties, reduced the necessity for 'crystal-ball gazing' or 'guesstimating', and has thus ensured ever tighter tendering in terms both of time and cost.

   The resulting legal effect is that the Contractor undertakes, by virtue of Clause 14.1, to carry out "the Works" in an orderly and regular manner and by methods of his own choosing, as "described by or referred to in" the Contract Bills – **NO MORE, NO LESS** – and to do so within the time period set by Clause 23. In executing the Contract, the Employer promises that if any changes occur, the Contractor will be compensated, by way of the 'claims' procedures set out in Clause 25 and 26, to additional time or money, or both.

Clearly, it would be morally as well as legally wrong for the Employer, and unprofessional for the Architect or Quantity Surveyor, not to allow the Contractor the full benefit of the promises made, by way of the claims procedures, for compensation in the event of changes actually occurring.

(b) If the change is due to an act or omission of the Employer, or the Architect acting on his behalf, namely Relevant Events 25.4.5, 6, 8, 12 and 13, a failure by the Architect to grant a proper extension of time would put time 'at large', and make it impossible for the Employer to recover any damages for non-completion under Clause 24.2.1.[55] Therefore, contrary to popular belief, claims procedures are incorporated into the Contract for the benefit of the Employer and not for the benefit of the Contractor.

(c) Where extensions of time relate to delays caused by Nominated Sub-Contractors, their triple role must be remembered:

  (i) As designers. The need to correct a design defect would require an Architect's Instruction, and the delay caused thereby would be a Relevant Event 5, which would entitle the Contractor to loss and/or expense, and not a Relevant Event 7, which would not do so.

  (ii) As suppliers of information. Delay caused by late provision of information would be a Relevant Event 6 which would entitle the Contractor to loss and/or expense, and not a Relevant Event 7, which would not do so.

  (iii) As constructors or installers. Delay caused in the actual carrying out of works is the only situation where Relevant Event 7, with the Contractor having no entitlement to loss and/or expense, would be applicable.

(d) Where extensions of time relate to delays caused by Statutory Undertakers or Local Authorities, there are two possibilities:

  (i) Relevant Event 11 would only be applicable where the delay is caused by a Statutory Undertaker or Local Authority acting "in pursuance of its statutory **obligations** in relation to the Works".

(ii) Relevant Event 8.1 would be applicable where the works in question had resulted from a non-statutory arrangement made with the Employer – e.g. diversion of mains, the installation of new mains, etc.

The difference is very significant because in the first case the Contractor is not entitled to loss and/or expense, whereas in the second case he is so entitled.[56]

(e) Clauses 25 and 26 are not necessarily related, because Clause 25 deals solely with delay issues, and Clause 26 makes no reference to delay, but only to what is known as 'disruption'. Consider the following scenarios:

(i) The Contractor will be able to complete early when, towards the end of the Contract, the Architect issues a variation instruction which, whilst it will disrupt the finishing work, will not prevent the Contractor from finishing by the Contract Completion Date. The Contractor would be entitled to loss and/or expense, but an extension of time will not be necessary.

(ii) In similar circumstances, if the delay will prevent the Contractor from finishing by the Contract Completion Date, he would be entitled not only to loss and/or expense, but also to an extension of time.

9. The Architect should remember that, when executing the Contract, the Contractor entrusts all decisions as to the quality of materials, goods and workmanship to him, subject only to the overview of an arbitrator. Therefore, if disputes on such matters should arise, the Architect's duty is to decide them in an impartial and independent manner, without consideration for the sensitivities of those involved, whoever they may be.

10. Towards the end of this Stage, the Architect should advise the client of:

(a) The anticipated Completion Date.

(b) The fact that when he issues the Certificate of Practical Completion, the Contractor's insurances will lapse, and he should ensure that his insurances will be in place simultaneously.

L 'Completion'

The following are some of the more important steps which the Architect should take at this Stage:

1. Carry out thorough hand-over inspections, and ensure that commissioning and testing of mechanical installations are carried out by Consultants.
2. Avoid issuing the Practical Completion Certificate before practical completion has actually been achieved. The term "practical completion" does not mean that the Works must be absolutely complete, neither does it mean that they need only be nearly complete:

> It seems on balance that the architect is justified in issuing his certificate if he is reasonably satisfied that the works accord with the contract, notwithstanding that there are **very minor** defects which can be remedied during the defects liability period.[57]

3. Provide Client with, and explain, maintenance manual.
4. Consider and decide whether or not the Completion Date should be revised, or further revised, and confirm the decision to the Contractor as required by Clause 25.3.3 of the Contract.
5. Monitor building and services during "bedding-down" period, in conjunction with Consultants if any.
6. Ensure prompt issue of, and compliance with, Clause 17.3 instructions wherever necessary.

M 'Feedback'

1. Carry out thorough inspection at end of Defects Liability Period, in conjunction with Client and Consultants.
2. Order opening-up and/or testing of any work, materials, goods or services suspected of being defective.
3. Prepare and issue a schedule of defects, within 14 days of end of Defects Liability Period.
4. Carry out thorough re-inspection, in conjunction with Client and Consultants, prior to issuing Certificate of Making Good Defects.
5. Refuse to issue Final Certificate if any doubt exists as to the existence of defective work, materials, goods or services.
6. Carry out feedback analysis.

All the papers arising in the course of the project should be sorted, all duplicates and other non-essential papers should be discarded, and the remainder should be preserved for at least 10 years. In particular, the Architect should make sure to preserve all 'state of the art' records – i.e. all technical information, regulations, manufacturers' recommendations, British Standards, etc., current at the time when the project was designed and constructed.

The Architect should carefully review, in conjunction with his staff, the Quantity Surveyor, Consultants, Clerks of Works and, if considered appropriate, the Contractor, all that has occurred during the course of the commission, in order to see what lessons are to be learned from the experience gained. Any changes to procedures which the review should suggest, should be logged for future reference and application.

Conclusion

If the foregoing recommendations are followed, there will be few, if any, claims; the Employer will get a better building, in better time and at a better price; and the Architect will have an easier, happier and more interesting life, with less risk of actions for negligence at the suit of the Client.

References

1 "The Placing and Management of Building Contracts", Report of the Central Council for Works and Buildings, London: HMSO, 1944, Paragraph 24, page 10.
2 ibid, page 28.
3 ibid, Paragraph 25, page 10.
4 ibid, Paragraph 26, penultimate paragraph, page 11.
5 ibid, page 28.
6 ibid, Paragraph 26, third paragraph, page 11.
7 ibid, Paragraph 47, page 19.
8 ibid, Paragraph 25, final paragraph, pages 10/11.
9 *The Plan of Work for design team operation*, London: RIBA Publications Limited (see extract annexed hereto as Appendix 3.)

10 *Architect's Job Book*, London: RIBA Publications Limited.
11 *Client's Guide*, London: RIBA Publications Limited, 1973. (See extract annexed hereto as Appendix 4.)
12 *Working With Your Architect*, London: RIBA Publications Limited, 1964.
13 "Survey of Problems Before the Construction Industries", Report prepared for the Minister of Works by Sir Harold Emmerson GCB KCVO, London: HMSO, 1962.
14 "The Placing and Management of Contracts for Building and Civil Engineering Work", Report of the Committee (Banwell), London: HMSO, 1964.
15 R & D Building Management Handbook *Preparing to Build*, London: HMSO, 1965. (See extract annexed hereto as Appendix 5.)
16 "Action on the Banwell Report", Building EDC, London: HMSO, 1967, section headed "The importance of time", page 3.
17 "Comparative studies of the construction industries in Great Britain and North America: a review", Building Research Establishment Current Paper CP 5/81, July 1981, I.L. Freeman.
18 ibid, page 6, in paragraph referring to "Productivity Team Report on Building", Anglo-American Council on Productivity, London, 1950.
19 ibid, page 10, in paragraph referring to "The American approach to contracting", Paper 8, E.C. Wundram, Conference on management in the construction industry organised for the RICS/IOB/BIM/DOE by Construction Industry Conference Centre Limited, London, 1977.
20 ibid, page 11, in paragraph referring to "Britain's high cost low speed building", Sir Maurice Laing, *Building Technology and Management*, 17 (5), ii–iii, London, 1979.
21 ibid, page 12, in paragraph referring to "UK and US Construction Industries: A Comparison of Design and Contract Procedures", Research Study by Reading University for RICS, London, 1979.
22 Per Lord Upjohn in *East Ham Corporation* v *Bernard Sunley & Sons Limited* [1966] AC 406.
23 "The Placing and Management of Building Contracts", Report of the Central Council for Works and Buildings, London: HMSO, 1944, Section 26, page 11, second paragraph.
24 Per His Honour Sir Walter Carter QC in *Moresk Cleaners Limited* v *Thomas Henwood Hicks* [1966] 4 BLR, at page 54.

25 ibid, at page 53.
26 RIBA Architect's Appointment, Clauses 3.5 and 3.8.
27 ibid, Clause 3.2.
28 ibid.
29 ibid, Clause 1.9.
30 ibid, Clause 3.2.
31 *Client's Guide*, London: RIBA Publications Limited, 1973, Section 4, page 17, first paragraph.
32 ibid, final paragraph.
33 *Working With Your Architect*, London: RIBA Publications Limited, 1964, page 14.
34 R & D Building Management Handbook *Preparing to Build*, London: HMSO, 1965, pages 20/21, Paragraphs 21 and 22.
35 *Working With Your Architect*, London: RIBA Publications Limited, 1964, pages 13/14.
36 RIBA Architect's Appointment, Clause 3.2.
37 ibid.
38 ibid, Clauses 3.7 and 3.8.
39 ibid, Clause 3.2.
40 By virtue of Clause 30.9.1.1 of the Contract, if the quality of any materials or standards of workmanship were to be described as "a matter for the opinion of the Architect" (Clause 2.1), the Final Certificate would be conclusive evidence in any proceedings that they were to the reasonable satisfaction of the Architect. This would be tantamount to giving the Contractor an indemnity for defective work! An architect should not allow himself to be exposed to the risks which this would involve.
41 *Sutcliffe* v *Thakrah* [1974] 4 BLR 16.
42 RIBA Architect's Appointment, Clause 3.2.
43 *Clerk of Works' Manual*, 1984 Revision, London: RIBA Publications Limited.
44 *Architect's Job Book*, London: RIBA Publications Limited, Section K6.1, page 124.
45 ibid, Section K5.1, page 123, and RIBA Architect's Appointment, Clause 1.23.
46 *Handbook of Architectural Practice and Management*, London: RIBA Publications Limited, 1965.
47 ibid, 4th Revised Edition, 1980, page 135.
48 ibid, page 368.
49 *Architect's Journal*, 3rd June 1981, page 1048, article by J.E. Cooke FRICS.

50 *Architect's Job Book,* London: RIBA Publications Limited, Section K2.3, page 115.
51 ibid, Section K2.1, page 111.
52 *Handbook of Architectural Practice and Management,* London: RIBA Publications Limited, 1965, pages 135–7.
53 *London Borough of Merton* v *Stanley Hugh Leach Limited* [1985] 32 BLR 51.
54 *Building Contracts,* 4th Edition, 1978, Donald Keating QC BA, London: Sweet & Maxwell, at page 347.
55 *London Borough of Merton* v *Stanley Hugh Leach Limited* [1985] 32 BLR 51, and per Salmon LJ in *Peak Construction (Liverpool) Limited* v *McKinney Foundations Limited* [1971] 1 BLR 114.
56 *Henry Boot Construction Limited* v *Central Lancashire New Town Development Corporation* [1980] 15 BLR 1, and *Boskalis Westminster Construction Limited* v *Liverpool City Corporation* [1983] 24 BLR 83.
57 *A Building Contract Dictionary,* 2nd Edition, 1990, Professor Vincent Powell-Smith, LLB(Hons) LLM DLitt Hons DSL FCIArb MBAE and Dr David Chappell MA PhD, London: RIBA, Legal Studies & Services (Publishing) Limited, at page 371.

2
Quantity Surveyors

The Quantity Surveyor's powers under the Contract, unless it is amended, are strictly circumscribed:

> ... his functions and his authority under the contract are confined to measuring and quantifying and (that) the contract gives him authority, at least in certain instances, to decide quantum, but (that) it does not in any instance give him authority to determine any liability, or liability to make any payment or allowance, unless such authority is given to him by Clause 31D(3).[1]

From this it might be thought that there is little that the Quantity Surveyor can do in respect of avoiding claims, but that would be quite wrong. Whilst the Architect is in the best position to prevent, or at least reduce, the incidence of claims in building contracts, and, if claims do arise, to prevent them resulting in disputes and the possibility of legal proceedings, the Quantity Surveyor can have a great deal to contribute in both respects.

Whereas his powers are strictly limited by the provisions of the Contract, the Quantity Surveyor can make invaluable contributions in the pre-contract period, and he can, without overstepping his powers, or trespassing on those of the Architect, make further contributions in this regard during the post-contract period, **provided** that he is properly appointed, and acts in a truly professional manner.

It is common for Architects to recommend the appointment of a particular Quantity Surveyor. Those who have in-house quantity surveying departments may recommend that a person from that department be appointed. Those architects who do not have such departments may recommend a person from an outside firm with whom they have worked in the past and have close ties. As explained in Chapter 5, an Employer, properly advised, should not agree to either of these recommendations. They can lead to 'cosy' relationships, there is a distinct possibility that the Quantity Surveyor will feel more loyalty to the Architect than to his Client and, regrettably, he may be influenced by hoping that, if he 'behaves himself', the Architect will recommend him for further commissions.

The essential point is that the value to the Client of the range of services which the Quantity Surveyor can provide throughout a building project, and in the avoidance of claims, are considerable, **provided** that he is appointed independently of the Architect. This point was emphasised in a Policy Background Paper issued by the Labour Party in the approach to the 1979 General Election. That Paper will be principally remembered for its proposals on nationalisation, but it had important things to say about the building professionals, and its relevance in the context of this chapter is what it had to say about the role of the Quantity Surveyor:

> Perhaps most important, quantity surveying should evolve into a genuine cost control function. At present the quantity surveyor has very little to do with cost control – he acts essentially as a translator of design drawings into quantitative terms from which a contractor can, however inaccurately, calculate a tender price. Quantity surveyors could instead become technical auditors, employed by the client and independent of the design team. Appointments could be made from a register of approved quantity surveyors, and not on the basis of architects' recommendations.[2]

There are now, of course, many Quantity Surveyors who offer these more general services, and, for the purposes of this chapter, it will be assumed that the Client has selected and appointed one of these.

Despite his independent position, it is of course necessary for the Quantity Surveyor to establish a good professional relationship with the Architect, and to co-operate with him at various stages, both in the pre- and post-contract periods. Furthermore, the Quantity Surveyor will have to act tactfully and diplomatically in following the various recommendations to monitor the work of the design team, if friction is to be avoided. If the Quantity Surveyor acts in this way, the Architect, who has so many duties and responsibilities, will probably be grateful for what he might otherwise have considered to be unwarranted interference.

As also explained in Chapter 5, a Client, properly advised, will require the appointment of the Quantity Surveyor to be made at an early stage; certainly no later than the beginning of Plan of Work Stage B, "Feasibility".

Despite the fact that his prime duty is always to his Client, the Quantity Surveyor must, in the post-contract period, not only act, but must be seen to be acting, with fairness to the Contractor when performing his duties under the Contract. He must never get a reputation for being a 'boss's man' because, if he does, it is likely to cause claims to escalate into disputes, and disputes to escalate into arbitration or litigation. Furthermore, on contracts where it is known that such a Quantity Surveyor is to be appointed, tenderers generally will increase their tenders as an insurance against the non-recoverable losses which they believe that they are likely to suffer as a result of unfair treatment.

Nevertheless, there is bound to come a time when disagreements arise between the Contractor and the Quantity Surveyor as to valuations. The Quantity Surveyor should never allow such disagreements to develop into arguments or haggling – they waste a great deal of time and money. But, more importantly, to do so would suggest that the Quantity Surveyor is insecure in his opinions, and that would increase the risk of the argument deteriorating into a dispute, and from that to arbitration. In any case, the Quantity Surveyor has no authority to do 'deals' with the Contractor, but only to apply the rules of the Contract, unless the Employer has expressly extended his authority.

The Quantity Surveyor must appreciate that when the parties execute the building contract, they jointly appoint him specifically to make decisions. Whilst he must of course listen to, and take due note of, what the Contractor has to say, he would be failing in the duty entrusted to him if he failed to make decisions and to stand by them. If the Quantity Surveyor has a reputation for fairness, and can demonstrate that he has fulfilled his duty to act with fairness, it is unlikely that a formal dispute will result because the Contractor will be advised that an arbitrator would be unlikely to disturb the decision made by such a Quantity Surveyor.

By acting positively in this way the Quantity Surveyor will do a great service to all concerned.

By way of a preface to explaining the particular contributions which the Quantity Surveyor can make in the avoidance of claims, it is thought desirable to draw attention to two important matters:

1. The "Plan of work for design team operation" (PoW) sets out the various stages through which a conventional building project passes from inception to completion, with explanations as to the functions to be performed at all these stages by those directly involved. It has been accepted by all those involved with building procurement. The principal purpose of the PoW is to show how a project should be progressed by methodical and systematic steps, so as to avoid abortive costs.
2. As explained throughout this book, and specifically in Chapter 1 – Architects, it is accepted by all authorities that the main cause of claims in building contracts is due to insufficient pre-contract preparation of the particulars of the work to be carried out.

The following are the particular contributions which the Quantity Surveyor can make regarding the avoidance of claims, by reference to the various PoW Stages.

A 'Inception'

1. On being offered a commission by a prospective client, the Quantity Surveyor should first of all discover the overall project programme as agreed between the Architect and his Client, and then consider whether the work required of him can be fitted in with his other commitments.
2. If no such overall project programme has been agreed, the Quantity Surveyor should point out the importance of having such a programme because, without it, the Client may have a quite unrealistic idea as to when the building may be started, and then, when the design stages take longer than he expected, he may well put pressure on the Architect and/or the Quantity Surveyor to speed up the process, and this could very well lead to insufficient pre-contract preparation.
3. If the time span which the prospective client requires for the project cannot be met, the Quantity Surveyor should consider whether or not it is possible for the brief to be modified. For instance, it is common for projects to be divisible into sections, as, for example, a low-rise housing development, or a building consisting of separated blocks. In such a case, the Quantity

Surveyor should suggest to the Architect and the prospective client that the project be divided into its parts, and each part treated as a separate contract.

This method, sometimes referred to as 'parallel working', has considerable advantages, particularly in terms of programming, because it enables the first part to be proceeded with whilst the next part is being detailed. Furthermore, it provides valuable protection against the possibility of the Contractor not coming up to scratch, or getting into financial difficulties. It also encourages low tendering and good performance if tenderers are told that, subject to his having given satisfaction, the appointed Contractor will be invited to negotiate a tender for the next and subsequent stage(s) of the project.

4. If the prospective client should object to the programme being too long, and the Quantity Surveyor is aware that he is bringing pressure on the Architect to speed up the process, he must explain the severe detriment which he would suffer from causing the building contract to commence without there having been thorough pre-contract preparation.

5. If the Quantity Surveyor cannot convince the prospective client that it would be in his best interests to allow sufficient time for thorough pre-contract preparation, or that the programme would not allow him sufficient time to do his job properly, he should seriously consider whether or not he should decline the commission. If he nevertheless decides to accept the commission, he should confirm his recommendations in writing, and couple that with a disclaimer of liability for all the consequences which will follow from the Client's requirements.

6. As the project advances, the Quantity Surveyor should monitor the overall project programme and draw the Architect's attention to any deviations. If it has to be modified, as a result of unexpected developments, the Quantity Surveyor should ensure that the reasons, and their effect, have been explained to the Client.

7. When accepting a commission, the Quantity Surveyor should:

   (a) Confirm that:

       (i)   He has no relationship, either professional or personal, with the Architect or any other member of the design team.

(ii) Whilst it will be necessary at various stages for him to co-operate with the Architect in order to monitor the work of the design team; to provide cost advice; to ensure compatibility between production information and the Bills of Quantities; and to enable him to provide financial reports to the Client; he will, where appropriate, act entirely independently of the Architect.

(b) Explain to the Client:

(i) The full range of services which can be provided, and how the provision of the full range would be in the Employer's best interests.

(ii) That until the Contract is let his sole responsibility is to the Client, but that that is no longer the case once the Contract is let, if he is appointed under Article 4 of the Contract. This is because, from that point on, whilst he will still owe continuing duties to the Employer, he will also have legal and professional duties to act independently and impartially as between the Client (Employer) and the Contractor. (The Quantity Surveyor should be sure to repeat this explanation immediately prior to the Contract being executed by the Client.)

(c) Agree his remuneration so as to allow for the full range of services which he is to provide, and he should ensure that the agreement is set out in a formal contract.

8. When the Architect has agreed the design brief with the Client, the Quantity Surveyor should be able to give cost advice, at least with sufficient accuracy as to enable the Client to decide whether or not to authorise the design team to proceed to the subsequent Work Stage B 'Feasibility'. Two types of case fall to be considered:

(a) The first is where the design brief has set out the Client's budget or cost limit, or that information has been added to the brief at the Quantity Surveyor's suggestion. In such cases, the Quantity Surveyor may be able to form a preliminary opinion as to whether or not the project budget is likely to be adequate.

If he is in any doubt on the matter, the Quantity Surveyor should immediately draw this to the attention of the Client and the Architect, with the recommendation that this aspect of the feasibility study be considered first, before the Client incurs the cost of its other aspects.

(b) The alternative case is where the Client has not set a budget or cost limit, but simply says: "This is what I want to build, how much will it cost?" In such cases the Quantity Surveyor may be able to form a preliminary opinion and give an approximate estimate of the likely cost of implementing the design brief.

As this is the first reference to the provision of approximate estimates, a few words of warning are appropriate. At various stages, the Architect will be under a duty to provide approximate estimates, and unless he considers himself competent in this area, he will, if properly advised, delegate this task to the Quantity Surveyor and fix him with liability for their accuracy.[3] Alternatively, the Quantity Surveyor's contract with his Client may impose a duty to provide approximate estimates direct to the Client.

In either case, the Quantity Surveyor should take very careful note of the following advice given by a leading authority:

> In the future therefore it appears that architects or quantity surveyors when giving estimates, or even "approximate" estimates, should make certain that the basis is clearly stated: does the estimate include for any possible increases in cost and, if so, the extent to which it does.[4]

The Quantity Surveyor should always play safe by giving approximate estimates in two parts: the first part, based on current prices; the second part, a prediction of all the likely ultimate cost increases, based on the anticipated contract period, full details of which should be set out and explained.

9. It may be desirable, in certain circumstances, such as when working for an inexperienced client, for the Quantity Surveyor to explain that whilst estimates will become progressively more accurate as the project develops, all must be considered as approximate, and that the true cost of a project will not be known until after the Final Certificate has been issued and the time within which that may be challenged by the Contractor has passed.

(The author was once involved in a case where the architect was held liable for failing to explain these and other matters in detail to his *émigré* Asian client.)

10. It is most important for the Quantity Surveyor to remember to regularly update an approximate estimate as the design of the project develops, as changes occur which affect the prediction of all the likely ultimate costs increases, or if the anticipated contract period is extended.

B 'Feasibility'

1. Whether or not the Quantity Surveyor has given preliminary advice on cost, he has a duty at this stage to prepare a formal feasibility report, in respect of which his functions are those set out in brief in the PoW:[5]

   2. (a) consider special site problems, access, etc.
      (b) appraise level of local building costs.
      (c) consider probable price trends.
      (d) assemble cost information on similar projects.
   3. . . . advise on feasibility of project in principle, including probable cost range, with quality indication if possible.
   5. Assist in preparation of report*; present feasibility statement in terms of cost range with quality indication: or confirm client's cost limit.
   8. Advise on tender procedure, and contract arrangements; assist in contractor selection†.

2. The feasibility investigations may reveal a problem(s) in the implementation of the brief within the Client's cost limit or the Quantity Surveyor's preliminary advice on cost. In such cases the Quantity Surveyor should consider with the Architect, and other members of the design team if necessary, the possible courses of action which might be taken to overcome the problem(s), in order that the Client may be advised.

3. If the Client accepts modification of the brief, the Quantity Surveyor should ensure that the Architect prepares a revised

---

* In accordance with earlier recommendations, the Quantity Surveyor's feasibility report should be made direct to the Client, and prepared after he has seen and considered the design team's report.

† Whilst it may be possible for the Quantity Surveyor to advise the Client on tender procedure and contract arrangements at this early stage, contractor selection is best left until Plan of Work Stage H "Tender Action".

brief including, if necessary, a revised project programme. The Quantity Surveyor should, if necessary, provide a revised approximate estimate in the two parts mentioned earlier.

C 'Outline Proposals'

The form which 'Outline Proposals' may take will vary with the type of project and, with a complex project, the Stage may consist of a series of development studies. Because this will be the first presentation of the design team's interpretation of the Client's brief, it is likely that alterations may be required.

1. The Quantity Surveyor should make sure that the Client has been advised that because the design team has a great deal of work to do in the next PoW Stage, in order to provide a fully developed design, the Employer should give the 'Outline Proposals' very careful consideration.
2. When the Client is finally satisfied with the 'Outline Proposals', the Quantity Surveyor should check to see whether or not they comply with the cost advice given in his feasibility report. If not, the Quantity Surveyor should prepare revised cost advice for the consideration of the Client prior to his authorising the design team to proceed to the next PoW Stage.
3. Finally, for the use of the Architect and other members of the design team during the next PoW Stage, the Quantity Surveyor should:

    Prepare an outline cost plan in consultation with [design] team, either from comparison of requirements with analytical costs of previous projects or from approximate quantities based on assumed specification.[6]

D 'Scheme Design'

1. This represents the final design stage in which input is required by the Client. As indicated in the 'Outline PoW' (Appendix 5), the work now to be carried out by the design team is:

    To complete the brief and decide on particular proposals, including planning arrangement, appearance, structural method, outline specification, and cost, and to obtain all approvals.

2. During this Stage, it is likely that the Quantity Surveyor will be consulted by the Architect, or other members of the design team, on aspects of the outline cost plan, as various elements of the design are considered in detail. If these consultations reveal a necessity to revise the current approximate estimate, the Quantity Surveyor should immediately inform the Client of the cause(s) and the effects.

3. The extent of detail which should have been prepared by the design team by the end of this Stage is set out in the relevant part of Chapter 1 – Architects, where references are made to the various authorities. It is, however, desirable to repeat the following:

   (a) Approval of the final scheme design marks the watershed of the design phase. Every requirement should have been worked out within the cost plan and agreed by all concerned, and it is normally unwise and certainly expensive to alter the design after this. About half of the design team's work goes into the following stage – the translation of the scheme design into working drawings and specification notes which between them exactly describe every detail of the building's construction – and much of this work will have to be done again from the beginning if any change is made in the scheme design after it has been approved.[7]
   (b) The architect will already have satisfied himself that the preliminary design solves all the client's problems and is technically satisfactory. But the design has now to be worked out in the minutest detail, by the designers by a continuous process of interchanging ideas and investigating alternatives for cladding materials, finishes, service installations and many other things. When every detail has been worked out within the cost plan, and agreed by all concerned, the design should be 'frozen', and not altered thereafter.[8]

   An identical message is given in a government publication addressed to all building owners.[9]

4. When he receives from the Architect what purports to be the final 'Scheme Design', the Quantity Surveyor should check that full details have been provided:

   (a) If full details have not been provided, the Quantity Surveyor should remind the Architect of his obligations in this respect, and should call on him to provide the missing details.
   (b) If full details have been provided, the Quantity Surveyor should check them against the outline cost plan so as to be able to confirm or amend the current approximate estimate.

5. When the Architect submits the completed 'Scheme Design' report to the Client, he should emphasise the importance of his

giving it detailed consideration, in the interest of avoiding abortive costs, prior to his giving approval and authorising the design team to proceed to the next PoW Stage. In doing so he should draw attention to the significance of the warning given at the end of the 'Scheme Design' Stage in the 'Outline PoW' (Appendix 5):

> Brief should not be modified after this point.

This point is so important that the Quantity Surveyor should add his weight to this warning when confirming or amending the current approximate estimate. Bearing in mind the abortive costs which could be involved, the Quantity Surveyor should, like the Architect, be particularly careful to obtain the Client's written authority prior to proceeding to the next Stage.

6. Finally, for the use of the Architect and other members of the design team during the next PoW Stage, the Quantity Surveyor should:

> 5. Prepare draft cost plan, on basis of scheme design and statements of quality standards and functional requirements received from architect and engineers.
> 7. In consultation, finalise cost plan, resolve anomalies and confirm.[10]

E 'Detail Design'

1. The activities at this Stage primarily involve members of the design team converting the 'Scheme Design' into a technical format by making final decisions on every matter relating to construction, materials and components. During this process, the design team will be checking their decisions against the cost plan.

2. The Quantity Surveyor's functions at this Stage are limited, but very important:

> 5. Carry out cost studies and cost checks. Inform architects and engineers of results immediately and give advice.
> 6. Provide interim cost check reports from time to time.
> 7. Provide complete cost check report.[11]

3. During these processes, the Quantity Surveyor should check to see whether or not they comply with his current approximate estimate. If not, the Quantity Surveyor should draw the

deviations to the attention of the Architect, and consider with him, and/or other members of the design team as may be appropriate, whether or not adjustments can be made.

4. However, no adjustments whatsoever should be made which will in any way cause a departure from the 'Scheme Design' approved by the Client.
5. If adjustments cannot be made without causing a departure from the 'Scheme Design', the Quantity Surveyor and the Architect should jointly report the matter to the Client, and explain the available options, which are:

(a) To amend the 'Scheme Design'.
(b) To increase the project budget.

If option (a) is chosen, the Architect will prepare a revised 'Scheme Design' which the Quantity Surveyor should check to ensure that the necessary adjustments have been made to bring the project within his current approximate estimate.

If option (b) is chosen, the Quantity Surveyor should provide a revised approximate estimate and a revised cost plan for the relevant design items.

6. The Quantity Surveyor should continue his cost studies and checks, and continue to provide cost reports until the Stage is completed, and he is satisfied that the 'Detail Design' is in accordance with his current approximate estimate.
7. It is of the greatest importance that the Quantity Surveyor should make sure that:

(a) The completed 'Detail Design' leaves nothing undecided which would require the inclusion in the Bills of Quantities of provisional measurements (other than those relating to ground works); avoidable Provisional and/or Prime Cost Sums; or provisions for Nominated Sub-Contractors or Nominated Suppliers, unless the problems which these would cause have been explained to the client, and he has approved of their inclusion.
(b) The Client has no last-minute thoughts regarding the 'Scheme Design', and the Quantity Surveyor should remind him of the significance of the warning given in the 'Outline PoW' (Appendix 5) at the end of Stage E:

Any further change in location, size, shape, or cost after this time will result in abortive work.

8. If the use of Nominated Sub-Contractors and/or Nominated Suppliers is really unavoidable, and their use has been approved by the Client, the Quantity Surveyor should ensure that the Architect has obtained tenders and that he (the Quantity Surveyor) has been consulted as to the financial effects.
9. Finally, the Quantity Surveyor can do a considerable service to the Client at this Stage so as to prevent post-contract delays, resulting in claims being made by the Contractor for extensions of time and loss and/or expense. He should check that the Architect:

(a) Appreciates that some materials or goods may have extended delivery dates, and that appropriate reservations may need to be made.
(b) Has made his decisions in respect of any Nominated Sub-Contractors and/or Nominated Suppliers as to the firms or companies which he intends to nominate. Also that he has obtained details of the relevant lead-in times, especially of those occurring early in the contract period, so as to enable him, if necessary, to give the Client a choice of options:

(i)   To postpone the contract start date, or
(ii) To pre-order so much of the lead-in time(s) as is necessary to avoid causing delay to the construction programme*. This procedure is envisaged by Clause 2.2 of the Employer/Nominated Sub-Contractor Agreement NSC/W.

The effect of not discovering the inability of Nominated Sub-Contractors or Nominated Suppliers to comply with the Contractor's programme until after the Contractor had been appointed would be disastrous, as illustrated in lines 1 and 2 of the diagram annexed hereto as Appendix 2. The two options are illustrated in lines 3 and 4. The financial consequences of such pre-contract non-discovery, compared with the results of adopting one or other of the options, are illustrated in a simplified example annexed hereto as Appendix 3.

---

*It should not be too difficult to estimate a likely construction programme prior to the appointment of a contractor.

F 'Production Information'

1. The principal activities in this Stage are the responsibility of the design team:

   > This [Detail Design] is followed by the preparation of production information in the form of drawings, schedules, specifications and any other information needed to convey to the contractors, sub-contractors and suppliers precisely what is required for every detail of the building.[12]

2. Apart from dealing with any cost problems which may result from the development of the 'Detail Design', the Quantity Surveyor will have no direct involvement during this Stage.

3. The Quantity Surveyor should enquire, from time to time, as to whether or not the preparation of the production information is proceeding in accordance with the overall project programme. If not, he should ask for an up-to-date forecast.

4. If the up-to-date forecast shows that the production information will be delivered to him later than was intended by the approved overall project programme:

   (a) The Quantity Surveyor should consider whether it would be possible to revise his own programme so as to have the resources available for the preparation and completion of the bills of quantities by the original date.

   (b) If such a revision would not be possible, the Quantity Surveyor should inform the Client of the cause(s) and the effect of the delay(s), and he should strenuously resist any pressure which may be brought upon him to take 'short cuts'. He should explain to the Client that taking short cuts would inevitably lead to insufficient pre-contract preparation, and the possibility of there being discrepancies in or divergences between the production information and the bills of quantities, both of which would be severely detrimental to his interests.

5. As will be seen from Chapter 5, a client, properly advised, should not authorise the Quantity Surveyor to proceed with the preparation of the bills of quantities until he has been assured by the Quantity Surveyor that:

   (a) Subject to minor queries, full details have been provided in the documents sent to him by the Architect.

(b) There will be no need for provisional measurements, Provisional or Prime Cost Sums, or provisions for unauthorised Nominated Sub-Contractors or Suppliers to be included in the bills of quantities.

Accordingly, the Quantity Surveyor should suggest to the Architect that, in order to avoid possible embarrassment, he should send a full set of the production information when it is ready, prior to seeking the Client's authority for the bills of quantities to be prepared.

If the Quantity Surveyor would be unable to give these confirmations, he ought to be able to resolve the problem(s) with the Architect and/or other members of the design team as appropriate.

6. If the Quantity Surveyor feels able to give the confirmations referred to, he should of course explain to the Client that whilst he appears to have all the information which he will require, he cannot be certain until he has started the actual process of preparing the bills of quantities.

G 'Bills of Quantities'

1. Whilst the preparation of bills of quantities is not a matter for this book, especially as the author has no quantity surveying qualifications, there are matters which it is appropriate to mention.

2. The Quantity Surveyor's role at this Stage is of crucial importance. If there is anything in the production information which the Quantity Surveyor does not understand, it is likely that the Contract Bills would not properly represent the works, and this would create problems, and possibly disputes, during the carrying out of work on site. If the Quantity Surveyor is in any doubt on any matter, or if he should discover any aspect of the work which has not been fully detailed or specified, he should immediately consult with the Architect, either direct, or by the use of query lists.

3. If consultations are direct, the Quantity Surveyor should take detailed notes of his queries and the answers which he receives, and send a confirmatory copy to the Architect. If consultations are by way of query lists, the Quantity Surveyor should carefully check that the answers which he receives cover the

actual point(s) which he raised. If not he should pursue the matter with the Architect until he is completely satisfied.

4. If the answers provided by the Architect require him, or other members of the design team, to provide further, or amended, drawings, details, schedules, specifications, and the like, the Quantity Surveyor should make sure that they are provided without delay. He should also ensure that they are incorporated into the set of production information, because it is most important that there will be no discrepancies in or divergences between the production information and the Contract Bills.

5. It is also important that the Quantity Surveyor keeps copies of all production information provided to him by the Architect and other members of the design team, duly date-stamped and registered. The reason is that architects often amend the transparencies of drawings and details without first taking and preserving file copies for future reference.

   The maintenance of such production information records is of even greater importance in the post-contract period, if amended drawings or details are issued, because, in carrying out his valuations, the Quantity Surveyor will want to know rather more about what exactly has been amended than he could ascertain from the amendment notes added to particular drawings.

   Furthermore, as the Contractor may not bother to keep copies of superseded drawings, those kept by the Quantity Surveyor may well be the only copies to remain in existence. Such records would be invaluable in the event, heaven forbid, that a dispute arose as to the valuation of variations.

6. Under no circumstances whatsoever:

   (a) Is the quality of any materials or the standards of workmanship to be described as a matter for the opinion of the Architect. The reason for this is explained in Chapter 1 – Architects, reference 40.

   (b) Is the term "equal or other approved" to be used in relation to any materials or goods.

   (c) Are any Provisional Sums or provisional measurements to be included without the problems which these would cause having been explained in detail to the Client.

7. The Quantity Surveyor will undoubtedly be consulted regarding both the form of contract and the manner in which it is to be

completed. In any event, he must ensure that this matter is finalised, and that the Client's approval is obtained, before the bills of quantities are completed, because this information has to be provided when tenders are invited.

8. The Quantity Surveyor should warn the Client of the dangers of unofficial amendments to the Contract, even if these are proposed by the Client's solicitors. Such amendments should only be made on the advice of experienced Counsel. If the Client should nevertheless insist on amendments being made, the Quantity Surveyor should give his opinion as to how tenderers are likely to react, and what financial consequences would be likely.

9. The following matters are those requiring particular attention in the body of the Contract:

(a) Whether the Contract is to be executed under hand or under seal.

(b) The names to be entered in Articles 3A (3B) and 4.

In this connection, it is bad practice to enter the names of firms. By the use of the singular throughout the Contract, in both cases, it is clearly intended that the names of particular persons should be entered. And, as a matter of law, only named persons can perform the duties entrusted to the contractual officers.

Furthermore, in Chapter 3 – Contractors, the technique of 'pricing the architect' will be explained. If the names of practices are entered, this pricing will be related to the member of that practice that the tenderers judge to have the worst "reputation for efficiency and fair play". It is therefore clearly in the interests of all, and particularly those of the Client, that the names of the particular persons who will in practice perform the duties entrusted to these officers should be entered in Articles 3 and 4.

(c) Clause 5.3.1.2. The Master Programme is to be provided prior to the execution of a Contract.

(d) Clause 25. No amendment should be made without considering the effects that this would have in relation to the fluctuation provisions.

(e) Clause 30.1.1.1. Whether or not a longer period than "14 days" is to apply.

(f) Clause 41.9. Whether or not this Clause is to be deleted.

10. All entries in the Appendix to the Contract have to be considered and set out in the bills of quantities, because they will be of importance to tenderers, but two matters require special mention:

   (a) The entries relating to "Date for Completion 1.3 (*sic* 23.1)", "Date of Possession 23.1", and "Deferment of the Date for Possession 23.1.2, 25.4.13, 26.1", should not be stated as "Subject to agreement". Definite dates should be given, and these should be the same as those in the "Preliminary Enquiry for Invitation to Tender".[13]
   (b) The Quantity Surveyor may also be consulted as to the entry for "Liquidated and ascertained damages 24.2". Even if he is not, he should make sure that whoever sets the figure fully understands the appropriate rules.[14]

11. As the bills of quantities are approaching completion, the Quantity Surveyor should consult with the Architect as to the firms or companies that they consider suitable to be invited to tender. Having arrived at a provisional list, they should carry out appropriate checks. Of particular importance for the Quantity Surveyor will be that the prospective tenderers have a good past record for co-operating in the carrying out of valuations, for providing necessary documents,[15] and such details as they may be requested to provide in order to enable the Quantity Surveyor to ascertain loss and/or expense[16]

12. The Quantity Surveyor and the Architect should jointly submit the proposed tender list to the Client for his approval. If the Client should ask for other firms or companies to be added to the tender list, the Quantity Surveyor and the Architect should exercise special vetting of any which they have considered and excluded, or do not know.

   If the Client should insist on the inclusion of any firms or companies against whom either the Architect or Quantity Surveyor raise objection, both should issue written disclaimers of liability.

13. A final decision as to the tender list must be made, in sufficient time to enable the "Preliminary Enquiry for Invitation to Tender", amended in accordance with the footnotes thereto, to be issued within "4 to 6 weeks" before the tender documents are to be ready for despatch.[17]

14. The Quantity Surveyor should send the completed bills of quantities, in draft form, to the Architect in order that he, and other members of the design team, can check the specification provisions, the list of drawings (especially any amendment numbers) to be referred to in the Third Recital to the Contract, and that there are no discrepancies in or divergences between any of the proposed Contract Documents.

15. Finally, the Quantity Surveyor should have the bills of quantities printed and inform the Architect that they are ready, and he will then seek the Client's authority to obtain tenders.

H 'Tender Action'

1. It is normally either the Architect or the Quantity Surveyor who will despatch the tender documents. If it is to be the Architect, the Quantity Surveyor should check with him to ensure that he will follow the NJCC Code,[18] and will use the recommended "Formal Invitation to Tender,"[19] amended and completed as necessary in accordance with the footnotes thereto.

2. The covering letter should draw the attention of the tenderers to rule that qualified tenders are not acceptable.[20]

3. If the Client requires that he, or someone else, is to despatch the tender documents, the Quantity Surveyor should explain to him the advantages of following the provisions of the NJCC Code.

4. If the tenders are to be delivered to the Architect, the Quantity Surveyor should ask to be present at the opening, and he should remind the Architect that:

   (a) No tender should be opened before the time given for their receipt.

   (b) All tenders must be opened at the same time, and as soon as possible after the time given for their receipt.[21]

   (c) The general rule is that, in order to prevent possible sharp practice, any tender which is received after the time given for its receipt has to be returned to the tenderer unopened.

   In the author's experience, whilst the reason for this rule is appreciated, there has been a great deal of complaint about its effects, bearing in mind that late delivery may be due to the vagaries of the postal service. Building owners feel that the returned tender may have been the lowest, and the affected tenderer feels that he has wasted a lot of time and money on preparing a tender which has not even been considered.

There is a simple answer to this problem. The tender envelopes, which would otherwise be blank, should be marked with a code number, or letter, related to the list of tenders. The time for delivery should be set at 12 noon. When the first post has been delivered, if only five out of six anticipated tenders have been received, the missing tenderer can be identified by reference to the coded list.

A telephone call can then be made to the tenderer whose tender has not been received, to explain the situation, and to say that if a copy of the tender is delivered by hand, or FAX, not later than 12 noon, it will be considered.

5. When the tenders have been opened, a list of tenderers, with their bids in ascending order of value, should be sent to the Client. The covering letter should remind the Client that:

   (a) The information is commercially sensitive and should be treated as confidential.
   (b) No tender should be accepted until after the Architect and the Quantity Surveyor have carried out important checks.

6. Even if the greatest care has been taken in the preparation of the various approximate estimates, it can still happen that the lowest tender is higher than the Client is prepared to spend. If the difference is relatively small, the Client may accept it, but if not, it should be possible to negotiate a reduced tender by making only minor alterations to the project. The procedure for such a "Negotiated Reduction of Tender" is fully set out in the NJCC Code,[22] and need not be repeated here. The Client must of course approve all such alterations.

7. If the difference is so substantial that it cannot be accepted by the Client, and negotiating a reduced tender would not be possible, there are two possibilities:

   (a) A complete reconsideration of the project, involving the Client, the Architect and the Quantity Surveyor would be necessary. If this course was successful, a modified scheme would have to be prepared, and fresh tenders would have to be invited.

(b) If no reconsideration of the project can be found which would be acceptable to the Client, the project may have to be aborted. This is the worst possible scenario, and is likely to lead to strained relationships between the Client, the Architect and the Quantity Surveyor!

The author has known it happen that the Client's agreement to competitive tendering has a 'hidden agenda', in that a builder that he has asked to be added to the tender list is the one that he really intends to appoint, but suspects that the builder might take commercial advantage if he were the sole bidder. What can then happen is that the Client may instruct the Architect and Quantity Surveyor to prepare a contract with that builder, even though he is not the lowest tenderer.

To accept a tender other than the lowest, unless there are very compelling and justifiable reasons, is bad practice, and a flagrant breach of the NJCC Code. The promise that its rules would be applied will have encouraged the other tenderers to invest considerable amounts of time and money in preparing their tenders.

To depart from these rules after tenders have been received is not only bad practice, it is tantamount to fraud, with which no reputable Architect or Quantity Surveyor would wish to be associated. Furthermore, the reputations of the Architect and the Quantity Surveyor for fair dealing are so important to them, and to all their future clients, that they should not in any case be sacrificed for the benefit of a client prepared to act in this unscrupulous manner. It is most definitely a resigning issue.

However, the realisation of the enormous problems which joint resignations would create at this Stage would bring most clients to their senses.

8. Assuming that such an unfortunate situation has not arisen, the Quantity Surveyor should proceed in accordance with the NJCC Code.

(a) The lowest tenderer should be asked to submit his priced bill(s) of quantities as soon as possible, but in any case within four working days,[23] and the procedure for the notification of tenderers should be followed.[24]

(b) The procedure for the "Examination and Adjustment of the Priced Bill(s)" is fully set out in the NJCC Code,[25] and need not be repeated here.

(c) However, there is a further matter which the Quantity Surveyor should take into account when examining the submitted priced bills, and this is to see whether or not there is any element of what is termed 'front-loading'. To allow any such front-loading to remain in the Contract Bills would be detrimental to the Client's reasonable interests, and could lead to disputes. The Quantity Surveyor should call on the lowest tenderer to correct any such front-loading, as a condition of the Quantity Surveyor recommending the tender for acceptance.

9. Having carried out his checks of the submitted bills of quantities, the Quantity Surveyor should report his findings to the Architect. However, he should not make his recommendation for the acceptance of a particular tender to the Client at this stage, because there are a number of important checks which the Architect will also have to make.[26] It is so vitally important, for the avoidance of claims, that these steps be taken, that the Quantity Surveyor should, to be on the safe side, check with the Architect that they have in fact been taken:

(a) The prospective Contractor's evidence of insurances has been obtained, and that the documents have been sent to, and approved by, the Client's insurance brokers and/or solicitors.

(b) The Contractor has agreed the dates for Possession and Completion.

(c) The Client has confirmed that the site will be handed over to the Contractor on or before the Date of Possession.

10. Only when all these checks have been made, and proved satisfactory, should the Architect and Quantity Surveyor recommend to the Client the acceptance of a particular tender, and seek the Client's authority to draw up the Contract Documents.

11. Because the difficulties for the Client in the event of a contractor becoming bankrupt, or going into liquidation, during the course of a contract are so considerable, the Quantity Surveyor should recommend that before accepting a tender, he should instruct his accountants to investigate and provide a financial report on the prospective Contractor.

12. At the same time, the Client should be reminded that up to this point, the Architect's and the Quantity Surveyor's sole responsi-

bilities have been to him, but that this will no longer be the case once the Contract is executed, if they are to be appointed under Articles 3 (A or B) and 4. From that point on, whilst still having responsibilities to him, they will also have legal and professional duties to act independently and impartially as between the Employer and the Contractor in a number of respects.

13. It is essential that the Contract Documents be prepared and executed by both parties before proceeding to the next Work Stage. It is also highly desirable that if the Documents are to be prepared by the Architect, the Quantity Surveyor should ask to be supplied with copies so that he can do a final check to see that there are no discrepancies in or divergences between them.

14. After the Contract has been executed, the Quantity Surveyor should:

    (a) Ensure that the Architect has notified all tenderers that a contract has been let, has told them the name of the successful tenderer, thanked them for submitting a tender, and supplied them with a list of all tender prices.[27] The list should set out the tender prices in ascending order of value, but no firm or company names should be associated with any of the prices.

    (b) Prepare, and provide the Client with, a cash-flow projection, as a forewarning of the likely value of Interim Certificates.

    (c) Obtain the Architect's agreement that he, the Quantity Surveyor, is to carry out valuations necessary for the purpose of ascertaining the amounts to be stated as due in all Interim Certificates,[28] and that it will be he who will carry out the ascertainment of direct loss and/or expense if that situation should arise.[29]

J 'Project Planning'

There will be little for the Quantity Surveyor to do during this Work Stage, except for the following:

1. Attend the first project ('pre-contract') meeting and establish lines of communication with the Contractor's surveyor.

2. Establish the dates on which the Architect will be under a duty to issue Interim Certificates,[30] and prepare a programme giving dates when, in order to comply with the provisions of the Contract, he will carry out his valuations.[31] The Quantity Surveyor should send a copy of the programme to the Contractor to enable his surveyor to be in attendance to take such notes and measurements as he may require.
3. Make sure that the Architect has:

   (a) Advised the Client that he must hand over the site on the Date for Possession, not interfere in any way with the Contractor or the works, not make any visits to the site unless accompanied by the Architect or one of his representatives, and make prompt payment on Interim Certificates.

   (b) Issued to the Contractor all documents referred to in Clauses 5.2 and 5.3.1.1 of the Contract, and nomination instructions regarding Nominated Sub-Contractors and Suppliers, if any.

   (c) Reminded the Consultants of their areas of responsibility for inspections of work on site, that they must not issue any instructions to the Contractor or any Sub-Contractor, except in an emergency situation, and that details of any instructions which they wish to issue must be provided to the Architect and the Quantity Surveyor to enable them to report to the Client as to the consequences, if any such instructions would constitute a variation.

   (d) Reminded the Contractor that he must not act on any instructions from anyone until they have been confirmed in writing by the Architect, except in an emergency situation.

   (e) Notified all manufacturers or suppliers of specified materials, products and systems, so as to ensure that problems are not caused by delayed ordering or the use by the Contractor of substitute materials.

K 'Operations on Site'

1. Whilst the Quantity Surveyor will have his own duties to perform, which are dealt with later, he can be of considerable benefit to the Client, and also of assistance in the avoidance of

claims, by monitoring the work of the Architect and other members of the design team during this crucial Work Stage:

(a) He should check to make sure that:
  (i) The Architect has planned to issue any outstanding production information as there may be, well before the dates required by the Contractor's Master Programme.
  (ii) The planned issue of outstanding production information is being met. If it is not, the Quantity Surveyor should forceably bring the matter to the attention of the Architect and remind him of the serious consequences which will result, in terms of claims.
  (iii) He is being provided with copies of all outstanding production information, and any supplementary information as the Architect may issue, at the same time as it is provided to the Contractor. On receipt, the Quantity Surveyor should check to see that the information provided is solely for the purpose of explaining or amplifying the Contract Drawings.[32]

  If the Quantity Surveyor should discover that there is any variation element in the information provided, he must immediately deal with it in the same manner as if the Architect had issued variation instructions, about which, see later.

(b) The Quantity Surveyor will, both from observations made at his site visits and from complaints which he may well receive from the Contractor and others, become aware if things are not going as smoothly as they should. In particular, the Quantity Surveyor should be on the lookout for situations arising which could lead to problems, as a result of the Architect:

  (i) Not dealing promptly and properly with notices served on him under the provisions of Clause 25.2 of the Contract*, or applications made to him under the provisions of Clause 26.1 of the Contract.

---

*The Quantity Surveyor should draw the Architect's attention to the effect on fluctuations of his failing to deal properly with Clause 25 notices.[33]

(ii) And Consultants and Clerks of Works, if any, not being meticulous in carrying out inspections of the works in progress.

(iii) Giving approvals other than in respect of aesthetic matters.

(iv) Acting out of sympathy if the Contractor is in difficulty, without having first obtained the Client's written authority.

(v) Accepting any 'botched' solutions or inadequate substitute materials which the Contractor may suggest if supply or other difficulties occur.

(vi) Conducting regular site meetings. The reasons why the Architect should not conduct such meetings are set out in detail in Chapter 1 – Architects.

If any of these matters come to the attention of the Quantity Surveyor, he should first attempt to resolve them with the Architect. If this is unsuccessful, his duty demands that he draw them, and their consequences, to the Client's attention.

2. Whilst a thorough review of the post-contract duties of the Quantity Surveyor would be inappropriate in this book, there are certain matters which it is thought should be discussed.

(a) Variations

The Quantity Surveyor should insist on being provided with a draft prior to the issuing of any instruction under Clause 13.2 of the Contract. This will enable him to give an estimate of the financial, and possibly also to give an opinion as to the time, consequences which would result from the issue of such an instruction. In some cases, it may be possible for the Quantity Surveyor to agree these matters with the Contractor.

In either case, the Quantity Surveyor should make sure that the Architect has passed this information to the Client when he fulfils his duty to explain the reason for it being necessary, or desirable, to issue a variation instruction, and seeks his permission to do so.

It is suggested in Chapter 1 – Architects, that before issuing an extension of time, the Architect should ask the Contractor if he would be willing and able to accelerate the work so as to bring the project back on course and, if so, at what price. It is anticipated that, before the Architect offered this method of avoiding claims for delay, and possibly loss and/or expense, to the Client, the Quantity Surveyor would be asked to express an opinion as to the alternatives.

(b) Expenditure of Provisional Sums

The Quantity Surveyor should also insist on being provided with details prior to the issuing of any instruction under Clause 13.3 of the Contract. As before, this will enable him to give an estimate of the financial, and possibly also to give an opinion as to the time, consequences which would result from the issue of the instruction, so that the Client may be advised if the Contract Sum would be increased, or the Date for Completion advanced.

In this connection, the Quantity Surveyor should be particularly careful if the proposed instruction relates to the expenditure of a "Provisional Sum for undefined work".[34]

(c) Valuation of Variations, Expenditure of Provisional Sums, and Remeasurements of Work covered by Provisional Quantities

It is in regard to valuations that the truly independent and impartial status of the Quantity Surveyor, and his reputation for fair dealing, will be of the greatest value in the avoidance of, or at least reducing the incidence of, claims leading to formal disputes.

There is no need to deal with the methods to be used by the Quantity Surveyor because these are fully set out in the Contract,[35] but it should be emphasised that the Quantity Surveyor should take care in regard to the following:

(i)   To apply the correct rule.
(ii) To warn the Architect that he should not authorise work to be carried out by 'Dayworks', either expressly or impliedly. He should also tell the Architect that if the Contractor should submit Daywork sheets, he should tell the Contractor that these have been forwarded to the Quantity Surveyor for his consideration.

(iii) To ensure that he attends on site to take such measurements as will be necessary for making his valuations, especially of work which will be covered up, as, for example, when the depth of a foundation excavation has to be varied.

(iv) For the reasons explained earlier, the Quantity Surveyor should never allow disagreements as to valuations to develop into arguments or haggling. To reduce the likelihood of such a situation arising, the Quantity Surveyor should be careful to explain, in as much detail as is necessary and appropriate, the basis on which the valuation was made, when passing it to the Contractor.

(v) It has been suggested that:

> detailed valuations need be made less frequently. Periodic payments should be made on approximate assessments which can be adjusted by exact valuation at quarterly intervals.[36]

It must be pointed out, however, that there is no justification for such a method in the Contract as it stands. All valuations must be carried out on an exact basis as soon as it is practicable to do so. If the work involved is to be carried out over an extended period, partial assessments should be made so that they may "be taken into account in the computation of the next Interim Certificate".[37]

A failure to carry out exact valuations at the proper time can lead to considerable argument, and possibly formal disputes, at a later date. For instance, if at the end of a project the Contractor realises that he has made a loss, or has not made as much profit as he had expected, he will argue vigorously as to the correctness of valuations made by the Quantity Surveyor, who will have great difficulty in justifying his assessments, especially if the essential evidence is covered up or no longer available.

Furthermore, the making of exact valuations at the proper time will considerably shorten the time which it will take to prepare and settle the 'final account'.

(vi) The Quantity Surveyor has no authority to do 'deals' with the Contractor, but only to apply the rules of the

Contract, unless the Employer has expressly authorised him to do so in specific circumstances.

(vii) To ensure that there is no 'falling between stools', as happened in a leading case,[38] by warning the Architect that he has made no allowance in his interim valuations for any defective work that there may be.

(d) Loss and/or Expense

If the Quantity Surveyor is instructed by the Architect to ascertain the amount of loss and/or expense incurred by the Contractor, or by a Nominated Sub-Contractor, the Quantity Surveyor should consult with the Architect in order to double-check that:

(i)   The application was made fully in accordance with the provisions of Clauses 26.1 and 26.1.1 of the Contract, or with the provisions of Clause 26.4.1.

(ii) The application related to one of the "matters" set out in Clause 26.2 of the Contract.

(iii) The Architect had, if necessary or desirable, exercised the power conferred on him by Clause 26.1.2 of the Contract.

If he is satisfied on these matters, the Quantity Surveyor should consider whether or not it is necessary for him to exercise the right conferred on him to "request such details of such loss and/or expense as are reasonably necessary for such ascertainment as aforesaid".[39] If the Quantity Surveyor makes such a request, he should specify the details which he requires.

It is neither appropriate nor necessary to deal with the methods to be adopted by the Quantity Surveyor in the ascertainment of loss and/or expense. If information is required, reference should be made to one of the specialist books on the subject, the authors of which are acknowledged experts in the field.[40] However, the following are of special importance:

(i)   The wording emphasised in the following extract from Clause 26.1 of the Contract:

> ... direct loss and/or expense in the execution of this Contract
> *which he would not be reimbursed by a payment under any other*
> *provision in this Contract* ...

The Quantity Surveyor must be careful to ensure that no double payment results from his ascertainment.

(ii) The Contractor may also become entitled to loss and/or expense by operation of the provisions relating to "Antiquities".[41]

In this case, the Contractor does not have to make an application but, if the Quantity Surveyor is to make the ascertainment, he must be instructed by the Architect.

(iii) The principles which have been referred to in respect of valuations apply equally to the ascertainment of loss and/or expense, regarding the avoidance of arguments or haggling; explaining the basis of each ascertainment; making exact assessments as soon as possible; making partial assessments where necessary, to enable the Architect to comply with the provisions of Clause 3 of the Contract; the advantages of exact assessments when preparing and settling the 'final account'; and the Quantity Surveyor having no authority to do 'deals' with the Contractor.

(e) Fluctuations – Clauses 38 and 39

In neither of these alternative clauses does it expressly provide that the Quantity Surveyor is to deal with the assessment of fluctuations, but it can be implied. The Quantity Surveyor should appreciate that his powers are limited:

(i) The Quantity Surveyor cannot act until after the Contractor has served written notice on the Architect,[42] and he has passed the notice to the Quantity Surveyor with a request that he carry out the assessment. Before starting on his work, the Quantity Surveyor should check with the Architect that the notice was in order.[43]

(ii) The Quantity Surveyor is given authority to agree with the Contractor as to what "shall be deemed for all the purposes of this Contract to be the net amount payable".[44] However, unless the Client has extended his authority, the Quantity Surveyor has power to determine quantum, but not liability.[45]

(f) Fluctuations – Clauses 40

Neither in this case is it expressly provided that the Quantity Surveyor is to deal with the calculation of fluctuations, but again it can be implied, from the wording of Clause 40.2.

In this case, the application of fluctuations is automatic, and not dependent on notice being given by the Contractor, or by the Quantity Surveyor having to wait for a request from the Architect before carrying out the assessment.

Again the Quantity Surveyor is given authority to reach an agreement with the Contractor, but in this case his authority is much wider,[46] subject to the two provisos.[47]

(g) Generally

As has been explained in Chapter 1 – Architects, the development of lump-sum contracts and related procedures has been increasingly to circumscribe and limit the Contractor's risks, and that this has been for the benefit of the Employer.

The resulting legal effect is that the Contractor undertakes, by virtue of Clause 14.1, to carry out "the Works" in an orderly and regular manner and by methods of his own choosing, as "described by or referred to in" the Contract Bills – **NO MORE, NO LESS** – and to do so within the time period set by Clause 23. In executing the Contract, the Employer promises that if any changes occur, the Contractor will be compensated, by way of the 'claims' procedures set out in the Contract, to additional time or money or both.

The Quantity Surveyor should appreciate that, when dealing with valuations, ascertainments of loss and/or expense, and fluctuations, it would not only be legally wrong, but it would also be unprofessional for him not to allow the Contractor the full benefit of the promises made, by way of proper compensation.

(h) Financial Statements

The Architect is under a duty to provide a monthly "Financial Statement" to the Client as part of his duty to "Keep client informed".[48] For this purpose, a "typical form" is provided for the use of the Architect,[49] from the headnote to which it will be seen that it is intended that the form should be completed from information provided by the Quantity Surveyor.

It is submitted, however, that, notwithstanding the Architect's duty, the Quantity Surveyor should send a financial status report direct to the Client at monthly intervals.

L 'Completion'

The Works having been completed, and the Certificate of Practical Completion issued, the Quantity Surveyor's work will largely comprise the finalising of the accounts. Sadly, even on projects which have gone relatively smoothly, problems do occur at this stage due to the sense of urgency being no longer a driving force. Whilst often not completely innocent themselves, Contractors frequently complain at the time it takes to achieve the settlement of accounts and the issue of the Final Certificate.

This problem should not occur if the Quantity Surveyor has kept up to date. It is at this stage that the benefits of dealing promptly and efficiently with valuations, ascertainments of loss and/or expense, and fluctuations, will be most valuable. Furthermore, the inordinate cost of finalising the accounts, which all too often results, will be significantly reduced.

The following reminders may be useful regarding the remaining stages of the Quantity Surveyor's work:

1. On the issue of the Certificate of Practical Completion, the Contractor is entitled to the release of one moiety of Retention. The Quantity Surveyor should notify the Architect of the amount to be released in the next Interim Certificate.
2. The Contractor has six months within which he is required to provide "all documents necessary for the purposes of the adjustment of the Contract Sum including all documents relating to the accounts of Nominated Sub-Contractors and Nominated Suppliers".[50] If the Contractor has also kept up to date, is anxious to arrive at an early settlement of the accounts, and there have been few, if any, Nominated Sub-Contractors and Nominated Suppliers, it should be possible for the Contractor to provide the necessary documents long before the expiration of the six month period.

The Quantity Surveyor should note that the reference is to "documents", not "information", which he should already have in his records.

3. As the preparation of the 'final account' proceeds, the Quantity Surveyor will find that "further amounts are ascertained as payable to the Contractor", and he should prepare valuations to enable the Architect to fulfil his duty to include the relevant sums in Interim Certificates.[51]

4. Within three months from receipt of the documents from the Contractor, the Quantity Surveyor is required to "prepare a statement of all adjustments to be made to the Contract Sum"[52] (commonly referred to as the 'final account'), and to send this to the Architect for him to send to the Contractor, with relevant extracts to each Nominated Sub-Contractor.

   Some quantity surveyors use two excuses for not complying with this provision in due time:

   (a) They wrongly interpret this to mean "three months from the expiration of the six months referred to in Clause 36.1.1".
   (b) They allege failure on the part of the Contractor to provide the necessary documents. This 'excuse' is only valid if, having received what the Contractor believes to be all the required documents, the Quantity Surveyor sends a list of any other documents which he requires.

5. The 'final account' will form the basis of the Final Certificate which becomes due not later than two months after the conditions for its issue have been fulfilled.[53] However, the Quantity Surveyor should remind the Architect that 28 days before he issues the Final Certificate, he must have issued a special Interim Certificate for the gross amounts due to Nominated Sub-Contractors,[54] the relevant details for which should be provided by the Quantity Surveyor.

6. It commonly occurs with public clients that instructions are issued that the Quantity Surveyor is not to finalise the 'final account', and the Architect is not to issue the Final Certificate, until after the accounts have been subjected to audit.

   Unless the Contract has been appropriately amended, such instructions are unlawful, because in executing an unamended Contract, the client body effectively waived any relevant Standing Order. The Quantity Surveyor and/or Architect would be in breach of their duties to the Contractor if they submitted to such instructions, and they should not do so.

In any case, the issue by the Architect of the Final Certificate in the sum which he and the Quantity Surveyor believe to be correct, does not deprive a client of any benefit which might have been provided by an audit because, if he finds a reason to disagree with the amount of the Final Certificate, he has his remedy at arbitration.[55]

M 'Feedback'

1. The Quantity Surveyor should sort all the papers arising in the course of the project, all duplicates and other non-essential papers should be discarded, and he should preserve the remainder for a period of at least 10 years. In particular, he should make sure to preserve all 'state of the art' records – i.e. all technical information, regulations, manufacturers' recommendations, British Standards, etc., which were referred to in the Architect's specification and incorporated into the Contract Bills.
2. The Quantity Surveyor should attend, and contribute to, any post-completion review which the Architect may call in order to see what lessons are to be learned from the experience gained. Any changes to procedures which the review should suggest, should be logged for future reference and application.

Conclusion

If the foregoing recommendations are followed, there will be few, if any, claims; the Client will get a better building, in better time and at a better price; and, like the Architect, the Quantity Surveyor will have an easier, happier, more interesting and more profitable professional life.

References

1 Per Webster J in *John Laing Construction Limited* v *County and District Properties Limited* [1982] 23 BLR 10, at page 14.

The Contract the subject of the action was the JCT Standard Form of Building Contract Private Edition with Quantities, 1963 Edition (July 1969 revision). However, it is thought that the extent of the Quantity Surveyor's authority would be the same in respect of JCT 80 – see the "Commentary" on the case in 23 BLR, at page 5.

2 "Building Britain's Future – Labour's policy on construction, A Policy Background Paper", October 1977, The Labour Party, Transport House, Smith Square, London, at page 56.

3 *Moresk Cleaners Limited* v *Thomas Henwood Hicks* [1966] 4 BLR 50.

4 Commentary to *Nye Saunders & Partners (a firm)* v *Alan E. Bristow* [1987] CA, 37 BLR, at page 93.

5 "Plan of work diagram 3 Col.4".

6 "Plan of work diagram 4 Col.4".

7 *Client's Guide*, London: RIBA Publications Limited, 1973 – see Appendix 6 of this book.

8 *Working With Your Architect*, London: RIBA Publications Limited, 1964.

9 R & D Building Management Handbook *Preparing to Build*, London: HMSO, 1965 – see Appendix 7 of this book.

10 "Plan of work diagram 5 Col.4".

11 "Plan of work diagram 6 Col.4".

12 *Client's Guide*, London: RIBA Publications Limited, 1973, paragraph 4, page 19.

13 Code of Procedure for Single Stage Selective Tendering 1989, National Joint Consultative Committee for Building, London: RIBA Publications Limited, Section 4.1, pages 2/3, and Appendix A.1, page 7.

14 See e.g. *A Building Contract Dictionary*, 2nd Edition, 1990, Professor Vincent Powell-Smith LLB(Hons) LLM DLitt Hon.DSL FCIArb MBAE Advocate, and Dr David Chappell MA PhD RIBA Legal Studies & Services (Publishing) Ltd.

15 Clause 30.6.1.1 of the Contract.

16 Clause 26.1.3 of the Contract.

17 Code of Procedure for Single Stage Selective Tendering 1989, National Joint Consultative Committee for Building, London: RIBA Publications Limited, Section 4.1.2, page 2.

18 ibid, Sections 4.2 and 4.3, page 3.

19 ibid, Appendix B, page 11.

20 ibid, Section 4.4, page 3.

21 ibid, Section 5.1, page 4.

22 ibid, Section 7.0, page 5.

23 ibid, Section 5.2, page 4.

24 ibid, Section 5.3, page 4.
25 ibid, Section 6.0, pages 4/5.
26 See Chapter 1 – Architects, H. 'Tender Action' paragraphs 1–8 inclusive.
27 ibid, Section 5.4, page 4.
28 Contract, Clause 30.1.3.
29 ibid, Clause 26.1.
30 ibid, Clause 30.1.3.
31 ibid, Clause 30.2, last paragraph.
32 ibid, Clause 5.4.
33 ibid, Clauses 38.4.8, 39.5.8 and 40.7.2.
34 See the various amendments to the Contract resulting from "Amendment 7, issued July 1988", and Rule 10.6. of SMM7.
35 Contract, Clause 13.5.
36 "Action on the Banwell Report", Building EDC, London: HMSO, 1967, paragraph 9.2.(iii), page 20.
37 Contract, Clause 3.
38 *Sutcliffe* v *Thakrah* [1974] 4 BLR 16.
39 Contract, Clause 26.1.3.
40 See e.g. *Building Contract Claims*, 2nd Edition, 1988 (reprinted 1989), Vincent Powell-Smith LLB(Hons) LLM DLitt FCIArb and John Sims FRICS FCIArb, Oxford: BSP Professional Books.)
41 Contract, Clause 34.3.
42 ibid, Clauses 38.5.1 and 39.5.1.
43 ibid, Clauses 38.5.2 and 39.5.2.
44 ibid, Clauses 38.5.3 and 39.5.3.
45 See reference 1, above.
46 Contract, Clause 40.5.
47 ibid, Clauses 40.5.1 and 40.5.2.
48 *Architect's Job Book*, London: RIBA Publications Limited, Section K5.1, page 123.
49 ibid, Section K6.1, page 124.
50 Contract, Clause 30.6.1.1.
51 ibid, Clause 30.1.3.
52 ibid, Clause 30.6.1.2.2.
53 ibid, Clause 30.8.
54 ibid, Clause 30.7.
55 ibid, Clause 30.9.3.

3

Contractors

Apart from sub-contractors, whose problems are dealt with in the next chapter, it is contractors who are most vulnerable in respect of claims. The reason is that under the Forms of Contract under consideration, contractors work on a credit basis, providing materials, goods and services for a period before they are paid. In other words, the Contractor finances operations and is always a creditor. At best the financing period is six weeks, but can be longer if the Quantity Surveyor undervalues, if the Architect fails to issue Interim Certificates, or if the Employer fails to make payments at the proper times.[1]

Contractors will be even more vulnerable in respect of any arbitration proceedings which he may initiate. Being a creditor means that if the Contractor cannot get satisfaction of claims through the contractual officers, or by direct negotiations with the Employer, and has to resort to legal proceedings, he will be the Claimant. The Contractor has no contract with the contractual officers and therefore, even if his claim relates to alleged acts and/ or omissions of the Architect and/or the Quantity Surveyor, arbitration proceedings must be against the Employer.

Arbitration proceedings are a very expensive matter for a Claimant. To start with, the Contractor will already be financing the capital sum outstanding on his claim. He then has to prepare full details of his case, together with supporting documents, and submit these to his solicitors who will almost certainly require the opinion of Counsel.

Counsel in turn may then call for statements from prospective witnesses as to fact, and for preliminary reports by Experts – Architect, Quantity Surveyor, Engineers, and/or others, depending on the type of claim. Preparation of such reports is a time-consuming matter. Having considered the Experts' Reports, Counsel will probably call for a conference with the Contractor, Solicitor and Experts, in his Chambers in London, when he will advise on the matter. Until then it may not be possible to serve a properly formulated Notice of Dispute on the Employer.

The Contractor's advisors then have to get an arbitrator appointed and, having done so, the Contractor will have to provide a sum of money as security for the Arbitrator's costs. If there is any doubt about the Contractor's ability to pay the Employer's costs of defending the action, the Contractor may also have to provide security for the Employer's costs. The Contractor then has to pay his advisors to attend the Preliminary Meeting which the Arbitrator will call.

The Contractor will then incur expense in respect of his advisors dealing with Pleadings – preparation of Points of Claim, considering the Respondent's (Employer's) Points of Defence, providing answers to the Respondent's Request for Further & Better Particulars of the Points of Claim, preparing Request for Further & Better Particulars of the Points of Defence and considering the answers provided.

The next step will be Discovery. This involves the Contractor listing all the papers in his power or possession, and one only has to consider the paper which is generated in building contracts to realise that this is a mountainous task. The Contractor must make these papers available for inspection by the Employer's Advisors. The Respondent has to provide a similar Discovery list which the Contractor's advisors have to inspect. The Respondent's documents will also be voluminous because they will include the papers of the Architect, Quantity Surveyor, Consultants, etc. Inspecting these papers is also very time consuming because it has to be carried out with great care:

It is commonplace in building and engineering arbitrations that documents thought to be wholly unnecessary from an evidentiary point of view and not worth copying for the purpose of the hearing may by the end of the evidence assume a crucial importance in supporting or rebutting the parties' contentions of fact.[2]

When Discovery is complete, Experts' Reports and Statements by Witnesses as to fact have to be finalised and exchanged with the Respondent's advisors. The Respondent's Experts' Reports and Statements by witnesses as to fact have to be considered and commented upon by all concerned.

The Contractor then has to pay his advisors for making all arrangements for the Hearing, which will include meetings of Experts of like disciplines, booking a suitable room for the Hearing, overnight accommodation for the Arbitrator, Counsel, Solicitor and Expert Witnesses, and making up a minimum of four sets of agreed documents, Reports, Statements, etc., for use at the Hearing.

As will be appreciated, this procedure is complex and takes months and sometimes years to complete, especially if the Respondent uses one or all of the many devices whereby the procedure may be delayed. Such devices are used by ruthless Respondents to make life as difficult as possible for the Contractor, sometimes with the deliberate intention of driving him into bankruptcy or liquidation.

Another device which is available to a Respondent to put the Contractor under pressure to settle at a sum less than the claim, is the making of an offer to settle, the equivalent of a 'payment-in' in litigation. The effect is that if the offer is refused, and the Arbitrator awards the Contractor a sum less than the offer, then the Contractor has to pay all the Arbitrator's and the Respondent's costs incurred thereafter which could be very considerable, bearing in mind that these will include the costs of the Hearing. When considering such offers, the Contractor will be reminded that:

> Arbitrators of great note in their own field can also have understandable difficulty analysing the underlying reasons for rules of substantive or procedural law, and can give way to impulses of sympathy or compromise producing anomalous and sometimes startling results. This instinct for compromise, and of reluctance to hold a claim wholly valid or invalid, is perhaps the most serious fault of non-legal arbitrators; it can work great injustice.[3]

Then there is the Hearing itself, with Counsel, Solicitor, Experts and Witnesses as to fact attending, and even in the simplest of cases this would last at least a week. There will then be a period during which the Arbitrator considers and then publishes his Award.

During the whole of this time, the Contractor will have to pay his advisors and Experts, none of whom come cheap, and interim charges made by the Arbitrator. The Contractor will not only have had to find the capital sums involved, but will also have incurred financing charges on those capital sums. Even if the Arbitrator finds in favour of the Contractor, his problems may not be over by any means:

1. Even those arbitrators who do not have an instinct for compromise may well err on the safe side by awarding the Contractor a sum less than his true entitlement.
2. The Respondent may take advantage of the Arbitration Act 1979, and lodge an application in the High Court for leave to appeal. In that case, the Contractor may not receive the amount awarded by the Arbitrator, or his costs, and will have to finance his defence to the High Court proceedings. The Respondent may lodge such an application on the most spurious of grounds, simply to encourage the Contractor to withdraw or settle, or even to go into bankruptcy or liquidation, due to the additional financial problems which this will cause him.

The final straw is that even if the Arbitrator finds in favour of the Contractor, and succeeds in his defence of the High Court action, he will only recover part of his costs, usually only 66–75%. Unless the award is substantial, the Contractor may be worse off, possibly far worse off, than if he had not gone to arbitration in the first place!

No apologies are made for having gone to such lengths to explain the extent to which Contractors are vulnerable in respect of claims, and the financial implications involved. It must surely be obvious that Contractors should do everything possible to avoid claims and the following are the cardinal rules and the procedures which should be adopted:

A Preliminary invitations to tender

In order to obtain more satisfactory tenders, selective tendering was one of the principal recommendations of the 'Simon' Report.[4] Adoption of this recommendation created problems when one or more of the selected builders declined to tender after receiving the tender documents. To overcome this problem, a Code of Procedure was issued in 1959 by the National Joint Consultative Committee for Building (latest edition 1989)[5] as part of which was the provision for issuing preliminary invitations to tender.[6]

Selective tendering and the use of the NJCC Code was commended in the Banwell Report,[7] and Action on the Banwell Report.[8] Builders should appreciate that selective tendering is very much for their benefit, and should give careful consideration to the Preliminary Invitation to tender. Accepting such an invitation only to decline to submit a tender after receipt of tender documents, for reasons which should have been known at the preliminary stage, is very bad practice, and could lead to the Architect not inviting that builder to tender on future projects.

Consideration of the Preliminary Invitation to tender should be in two stages:

1. Pricing the Architect

The Preliminary Invitation to tender will reveal the names of the Architect and the Quantity Surveyor. These persons will be the contractual officers, and due performance of their functions and duties is crucial to the avoidance of claims. As a first step, therefore, it is their track record, and particularly that of the Architect, which must be considered. This consideration should be based on what a leading speaker had to say at a conference convened by the Faculty of Building at The Royal Society:

> Dare I tell you that we Builders not only price the Bill of Quantities – we also price the Architect, so that one with a reputation for efficiency and fair play will produce a lower tender for his Client.[9]

'Pricing the Architect' means checking the track record of the Architect, both from the builder's own experiences and from information gleaned from other builders and on the grapevine.

The questions to be asked include: does the Architect have a reputation for:

(a) Carrying out the duties imposed on him by the Contract correctly and at the proper time?
(b) Acting in a wholly independent and impartial manner in respect of those provisions of the Contract which require him to form opinions, in particular in respect of extensions of time and loss and/or expense?
(c) Issuing outstanding information in good time?

(d) Instructing the Quantity Surveyor in respect of valuations for Interim Certificates and the ascertainment of loss and/or expense?

If the answer to any of these questions is in the negative, the builder should foresee trouble. However, even if the answers to all of these questions are in the affirmative these further questions are important: does the Architect have a reputation for:

(a) Postponing decision making by relying on his ability to issue variation instructions, and by introducing an excessive number of Nominated Sub-Contractors?
(b) Failing to confirm instructions issued "otherwise than in writing"?

If the answer to either of these questions is in the affirmative, the builder should foresee major managerial problems if he is the successful tenderer and became the Contractor.

The track record of the Quantity Surveyor should also be checked in a similar manner. The questions here to be asked include, does he:

(a) Prepare proper valuations* for Interim Certificates, including precise valuations of the effect of Architect's Instructions and ascertainment of loss and/or expense?
(b) Act in a wholly independent and impartial manner in respect of those provisions of the Contract which give him a discretion as to the method of valuation?

Of all these questions, the most important one is, despite the obvious vested interest which they have in their own decisions, do both contractual officers have a reputation for strict compliance with their professional and legal duties to act in a wholly independent and impartial manner; are prepared to stand up to the Employer; or do either or both of them have a reputation for being 'boss's men'?

---

*Even though the Contract provides for exact valuations, there are quantity surveyors who only make approximate monthly valuations. This results in the amount of retention being progressively increased above the contractual percentage, and this will make the Contractor even more vulnerable to non-recoverable losses if a dispute does arise, especially after the Works have been completed. One authority has said that exact valuations must in any case be made at not more than quarterly intervals.[10]

Appendix A.1 to the Preliminary Invitation to tender will also reveal the names of any:

(a) Consultants who are to be given supervisory duties. Whilst they will not be contractual officers, and can act only through the Architect, efficient performance of their functions and duties is crucial to the avoidance of claims.
(b) Major Nominated Sub-Contractors who have already been selected. As builders will know better than anyone, Nominated Sub-Contractors frequently cause major problems in building contracts.

The track record of such Consultants and Nominated Sub-Contractors should also be checked.

Finally, and probably most importantly, builders would be well advised to 'price' the prospective Employer. Not only should his credit rating be checked, but his track record on previous contracts should be investigated. For instance, does he have a reputation for demanding higher standards than those allowed for in the Contract Documents, changing his mind at short notice as the project proceeds, making delayed payments, arguing over the amount of the Final Certificate, etc?

2. General Matters

The builder should very carefully consider all the technical information given in Appendix A.1 to the Preliminary Invitation to tender. Provided this has been properly completed, the builder will know, amongst other things, the approximate date for the despatch of tender documents, the tender period, the site location, the type of project, the estimated cost range, the form of contract, the anticipated date for possession and the intended contract period. From this information, the builder will know if there are any reasons from the legal, technical, managerial and current workload aspects, whether or not the invitation should be accepted.

Finally, Appendix A.1 will say whether or not provision for Liquidated Damages and Performance Bond will be included in the Contract and, if so, the proposed amounts. It will also give the period for which the tenders are to remain open for acceptance. These financial matters should also be considered.

Having done this basic research, the builder must decide on how to respond to a preliminary invitation to tender. In appropriate circumstances he may decline to tender, or he may decide to accept the invitation to tender, knowing that he will have to add a percentage to his tender in order to make provision for the non-recoverable damage which his research indicates he might suffer if he became the Contractor.

Circumstances may dictate that the builder should accept the invitation and submit a competitive tender, despite unfavourable indications. If he does so, he should know that he will have to provide very efficient management procedures to eliminate, or at least reduce, suffering non-recoverable damage.

A builder does not have to explain why he declines a Preliminary Invitation to tender and, whatever the reason, he should not be afraid to do so, bearing in mind what is said in Appendix A.1:

> Your inability to accept will in no way prejudice your opportunities for tendering for further work under my/our direction;

The builder's circumstances may change after acceptance of the Preliminary Invitation to tender, making it necessary to withdraw. The procedure for the withdrawal of acceptance is provided for in the NJCC Code:

> Once a contractor has signified initial agreement to tender it is in the best interests of all parties that such acceptance should be honoured. If in exceptional circumstances a contractor has to withdraw his acceptance he should give notice of this intention before the issue of tender documents.[11]

B On receipt of tender documents

1. Checking tender documents

On receipt of the tender documents the following checks should be made to see whether:

(a) The formal invitation to tender follows the provisions of the NJCC Code.[12] A check should be made to see whether or not this is so. If it does follow the Code, consideration should be given to all aspects of the rules. If it does not follow the Code, careful consideration should be given to the details of the invitation in order to decide on estimating policy.
(b) Any of the details provided in the Preliminary Invitation to tender have been varied.

(c) The details provided in the tender documents reveal matters which were not anticipated from the Preliminary Invitation to tender.

The result of this checking could lead the builder to reconsider his acceptance of the Preliminary Invitation to tender. This situation is provided for in the NJCC Code. In these circumstances:

> ... notice should be given not later than two working days after receipt of the tender documents.[13]

In order to comply with this provision, it is important that the builder should make a general appraisal of the tender documents immediately after they are received.

If circumstances arise after the two day period which make it impossible to submit a tender, the builder should inform the Architect at once. Provided that the reasons are bona fide, the builder should not be penalised. The builder should never conceal his withdrawal by taking a 'cover'. This is extremely bad practice because it distorts the purpose of selective tendering and, if discovered, will almost certainly result in the builder being struck off the Architect's tender list, and it will also adversely affect his general reputation.

2. Detailed check of tender documents

As long ago as 1944, the 'Simon' Report stated that the principal cause of claims and disputes in the building industry was:

> (a) Insufficient pre-contract preparation of the particulars of the work to be carried out.[14]

Yet despite the time which has elapsed, and the extent to which this knowledge has been publicised, it is still true to say that it is inadequate pre-contract preparation which is the principal cause of disputes and claims.

Therefore, in addition to considering the usual matters, such as contract conditions, timescale, remoteness of site, site restrictions, unfamiliar materials products and systems, plant and manpower requirements, etc., the estimator should give careful consideration to the extent to which the project details have been prepared.

The 'Simon' Report said that:

> In all cases it is of the utmost importance that full and detailed drawings, specifications, bills of quantities and estimates (from Nominated Suppliers

and Nominated Sub-Contractors) should be prepared before the main contract is let ....[15]

Ideally, therefore, production information from all sources, including Consultants, proposed Nominated Suppliers and Sub-Contractors should be complete and integrated. Sadly, this is often not the case and the estimator should assess the extent of inadequate pre-contract preparedness in order to anticipate the likelihood of late instructions and numerous variations. The estimator will then be able to allow for the establishment of on- and off-site management procedures and systems which will be necessary.

The benefit of this research is often lost because the resulting assessment has not been preserved by the estimator and passed to the contract management team when a tender is successful. It is important that such 'falling between stools' is avoided.

The following will assist the estimator in assessing the degree of preparedness of the proposed works.

(a) Where only general arrangement drawings are provided, the estimator should take advantage of the invitation to inspect further drawings and details[16] in order to assess the thoroughness of their preparation, including production information from Consultants.

(b) Consider the number, type and proportion of work referred to as "Approximate Quantity" and those covered by Provisional Sums for 'undefined' work[17] included in the Bills of Quantity.

(c) If there are to be Nominated Sub-Contractors and/or Nominated Suppliers, have these been decided? If so, consider their record in respect of co-operation and efficiency, and whether or not they have proper quality control procedures. A check should also be made as to whether or not all production information from these sources is available.

C Post-tendering

1. Types of Contract

There are only two types of contract in English Law:

(a) A 'speciality contract', or deed. Such a contract only comes into existence when the document is executed, i.e. in accordance with the Law of Property (Miscellaneous Provisions) Act 1989.

(b) A 'simple contract'. Such contracts, which are the most common type, do not have to follow any special form. For instance, in addition to the execution of a formal document, they may be entered into orally, by an exchange of letters, or even by no more than conduct. However, for a contract as complex as a building project, builders should always insist on formal documentation.

   For a 'simple contract' to come into existence, three conditions must be fulfilled: 'Offer', 'Acceptance' and 'Consideration'. In building contracts a builder's tender is an 'Offer' and the tender price is 'Consideration'. 'Acceptance' occurs when the building owner accepts the builder's tender. But it is frequently not that straightforward, and it must be appreciated that 'Acceptance' must be both unequivocal and unconditional.

2. Avoiding 'Acceptance'

An 'Offer' can be withdrawn at any time prior to 'Acceptance'. But builders should be aware that if a tender is accepted, they will be bound in contract, and cannot then either correct estimating errors or withdraw the tender. Tenders should therefore be double-checked before submission.

   There is frequently a considerable delay between the submission of a tender and its acceptance. An 'Offer' will be withdrawn automatically if the tender includes a time limit within which it is open for 'Acceptance'. Where this has not been done, a builder would be well advised to check the basis of his tender to see whether or not it should be withdrawn or amended.

   If the NJCC Code is being operated, builders will be protected at two stages against being bound in an unsatisfactory contract:

(a) Prior to acceptance of his tender, "The lowest tenderer" will "be asked to submit his priced bill(s) of quantities".[18] The tenderer should take advantage of this opportunity for a tender to be rechecked before submitting the priced bills.
(b) The Quantity Surveyor will examine the lowest tenderer's priced bill(s) of quantities "to detect errors in computation of the tender".[19] The builder will then be informed of any errors which have been detected, and will be given whichever of the options are afforded by the Alternatives.[20]

A most important part of the Contract is that the Contractor is likely to be under an obligation to complete the Works by the Completion Date and, if he fails in this obligation, he will be liable for liquidated and ascertained damages. Checking the basis of the tender should, therefore, in addition to a consideration of prices, also entail careful consideration as to whether this obligation as to time can be achieved, by preparing an outline Master Programme. If not, the builder should ask for the Completion Date to be revised, as a condition to the confirmation of his tender.

If the builder knows that all the necessary information will be available at the commencement of the Contract, because there has been thorough pre-contract planning by the design team, the preparation of an outline Master Programme will principally be for internal use and reassurance.

However, where there has been inadequate pre-contract planning by the design team, it is important that the builder should submit the outline Master Programme to the Architect, and this should be clearly marked with the dates by which each piece of outstanding information will be required. By this means, the Architect may be brought to realise that he cannot provide the outstanding information to suit the builder's proposed programme, and that a revised Completion Date will be necessary.

Amongst the matters to be considered in preparing the outline Master Programme are the availability of Domestic Sub-Contractors, delivery periods required by Domestic Suppliers of specified goods and/or materials, and the effect of commitments on other contracts as they affect plant, labour, supervisory and administrative resources, etc.

3. Amended tenders

It is not uncommon for an architect to say that a builder's tender is accepted subject to conditions, such as a list of additions or omissions, or by way of Addendum Bills of Quantities. That would not be 'Acceptance' – it would be a 'Counter-Offer'. 'Acceptance' would occur if the builder accepted the 'Counter-Offer'. But the builder is under no obligation to do so, and it is open to him to make a 'Counter-Counter-Offer' if he so wishes.

Where a builder's tender is not accepted as submitted, negotiations often take place until finally the parties believe that they are agreed. However, when the pressure is off, it is remarkable how often the parties subsequently argue as to what was actually agreed. This could lead to the builder finding himself involved in what is generally known as a "battle of forms", and such battles often finish up in the Courts with all that that involves.

In these circumstances the builder should be very careful to make sure that the final agreement is made clear beyond all doubt by the preparation of formal Contract Documents. Furthermore, it is essential that the builder should make it quite clear that he will take no action, either on- or off-site, until the Contract Documents have been executed by both parties.

4. Letters of intent

It is common for a builder to receive a letter from the Architect, saying that his Client intends in due course to accept the builder's tender. Such letters are known as 'letters of intent', and they do not constitute 'Acceptance'. The builder should not take any action on the strength of such a letter which would lead to expense, because, there being no actual contract, there is no guarantee of reimbursement.

Most importantly, the builder should not place any orders for goods, materials or services, because, if the promised contract does not materialise, he could have sub-contract and/or supplier costs which he would be unable to avoid paying.

However, if there is a rider to the letter, such as "In the meantime please proceed to demolish building A", the builder would be entitled to payment for that work even if the promised contract did not materialise.

D Execution of Contract Documents

Once a formal contract has been executed, it is extremely difficult, if not impossible, for errors to be corrected. Yet it is not uncommon for there to be differences between the documents presented for execution and those on which the tender was based. For this reason, the builder should insist on the Contract Documents being prepared and presented for checking and execution before he commits himself to placing orders and commencing work on site.

On receipt of the Contract Documents, it is vital that the builder should check very carefully to see that the Contract Documents are identical in every respect to the documents on which he tendered.

1. Form of Contract

This should be checked against the schedule set out in the Contract Bills. The Articles should be checked, particularly the list of drawings, and their amendment letters, used in the preparation of the Contract Bills. All Conditions should be checked, especially any that have been deleted, amended or added. All entries in the Appendix should be checked, especially "Date for Completion", "liquidated and ascertained damages", "Period of Interim Certificates", "Period of Final Measurement and Valuation", and "Fluctuations".

2. The Contract Bills

These should be checked, page by page and item by item, especially the Preliminaries and the quantities and rates sections, to see that they are identical with those on which the tender was based, taking special care where an Addendum Bill is incorporated.

3. The Contract Drawings

These should be checked, firstly to see that the numbers and their amendment letters correspond to those listed in the Contract Bills and, secondly, to see that there are no unrecorded amendments.

4. Comparison of Contract Documents

A very careful check should be made to ensure that there are no discrepancies or divergences between any, or any parts, of the Contract Documents. In this connection it is important to check what is shown on the Contract Drawings against what is described in the specification sections of the Contract Bills.

5. Concluding stages

(a) If there are any differences between the Contract Documents and the tender documents, or if there are any discrepancies or divergences between any, or any parts, of the Contract Documents, the builder should obviously get these matters resolved before executing the Contract Documents.

(b) It is common practice for the Contract Documents to be sent to the builder for execution first and to the building owner afterwards. The builder should execute the Contract Documents and return them to the Architect promptly. In his covering letter he should make it quite clear that he will take no action, either on- or off-site, until he has received a copy of the Documents after they have been executed by the building owner.

(c) In executing the Contract Documents, the builder should not only have completed the attestation clause in the Contract and signed the Contract Bills (and Addendum Bills if any) and each of the Contract Drawings, he should also have initialled all deletions, amendments, entries and additions, to the printed or typed words. When in due course he receives the copy of the Contract Documents the builder should check to make sure that the building owner has done likewise. He should also check to see that they are identical to those which he executed.

(d) The copy Contract Documents as provided should be placed in a safe place, under lock and key, and not used for any purpose other than for reference by top management. (Further copies of the Contract Drawings and unpriced bills of quantities will be required to be kept on site, in accordance with Clause 5.5, but only the builder's surveyor should have a copy of the Contract Bills.)

Once the Contract Documents have been executed, the building owner and the builder are referred to as the "Employer" and "Contractor" respectively, and as "the parties" collectively.

E Project Planning

1. Master Programme

The Contractor's Master Programme should have been submitted to, and approved by, the Architect during the post-tendering, pre-contract, stage. However, if this was not done, the preparation of the Master Programme is the first step which should now be taken, even if Clause 5.3.1.2 has been deleted. The Master Programme should be in network analysis form, with the critical path clearly indicated, for the following reasons:

(a) It is easier to monitor progress against prediction, and thus to enable management to increase or amend resources before progress is seriously affected.
(b) It enables the effects of delaying factors to be estimated and the critical path to be checked and, if necessary, reassessed and redirected.
(c) It provides invaluable support for any notices under Clause 25.2 and, where appropriate, applications under Clause 26.1, in the event of delays caused by Relevant Events.

The Master Programme is not a Contract Document, and it does not therefore bind the Contractor. It can be varied at any time to suit developments as and when they occur. If he does vary the Master Programme, the Contractor must send revised copies to the Architect, and to any other person who has been provided with the original. Whilst he has the right to vary the Master Programme, the Contractor must not do so in such a way as to affect adversely those who have planned their work on the basis of the original.

Preparation of the Master Programme will be relatively straight-forward if the Contractor has been provided, at the commencement, with all the information necessary to enable him to complete the Works.

Where this is not so, the Contractor should prepare, and submit to the Architect, a list of all outstanding information, together with the dates by which each piece is required. These dates should be clearly indicated on the Master Programme.[21] The dates should be realistic; i.e. "neither unreasonably distant from nor unreasonably close to the date on which it was necessary for him (the Contractor) to receive the same." – Clauses 25.4.6 and 26.2.1 of the Contract.

There will be circumstances in which the Contractor will not know the dates on which he will require certain information. The most common case is where there is a P.C. Sum for goods or materials. With the best will in the world, the Contractor will have no way of knowing the delivery periods which will apply to the actual goods or materials which he will ultimately be instructed to order.

Where this is so, the Contractor should inform the Architect, in writing, that the dates which he has given in respect of such matters are no more than 'guesstimates', which he cannot be held to. The Architect will then have been put on notice that he must make his selections and establish delivery times as early as possible, in order to be able to issue instructions in good time.

As regards outstanding information, there are various other matters which the Contractor should note:

(a) Strictly speaking, the Contractor is under no obligation to ask for outstanding information. Under Clause 5.4 of the Contract, it is the Architect's duty to provide outstanding information whether or not the Contractor makes application. Nevertheless, if the Contractor knows of further information which he will require, his failure to apply for that information at the appropriate time may be taken into account by the Architect in respect of any notice under Clauses 25.2 and 25.4.6, and/or any application under Clauses 26.1 and 26.2.1, that he may receive from the Contractor.

(b) Situations may occur where the Contractor may not discover the need for additional information until the relevant piece of construction is being carried out. The Contractor should do all that he can to avoid such a situation from arising because, if it leads to delay, it is bound to result in a dispute as to whether:

   (i)   The Architect should have provided the additional information without the Contractor having to make an application, or

   (ii) The Contractor should have known, at an earlier stage, that the additional information would be required.

(c) The Contractor may know of information which he will require, but genuinely believes that this will be forthcoming from the Architect without his needing to apply for it. But the Architect, equally genuinely, believes that he has provided all outstanding information. This unfortunate 'falling between stools' can all too easily lead to disputes. The Contractor can avoid this by asking the Architect, in writing, to inform him when he issues what he believes is the last of the outstanding information. The Contractor will then be on notice that if there is anything further which he requires he must apply for it.

2. Information

Immediately after the execution of the Contract, the Architect must provide, in addition to a copy of the Contract Documents, working copies of the Contract Drawings and the Bills of Quantities (Clause 5.2.2).

The Contractor should check these in order to see that they are identical to the Contract Documents.

If he has not already done so, the Architect must provide descriptive schedules and other like documents so soon as is possible after the execution of the Contract (Clause 5.2.3). When these are provided, they should be checked to see whether they are by way of explaining or amplifying the Works covered by the Contract Documents. It is not unknown for this further information to require work(s) in addition to that covered by the Contract Documents. Where this is discovered, the Contractor should immediately remind the Architect of Clause 5.3.2 of the Contract, and ask that he either delete the additional work(s) or issue an Architect's Instruction under Clause 13.2 of the Contract.

If the schedules and other like documents are not provided at this stage, and the Contractor knows that they will be required, they should be included in the list of outstanding information referred to earlier.

3. Nominated Sub-Contractors

Where there has been thorough pre-contract preparation, the Architect should be in a position to issue instructions regarding all Nominated Sub-Contractors at this stage. It is therefore appropriate to deal with this matter now. The situation where there has not been thorough pre-contract preparation, resulting in nomination instructions being issued post-contract, will be discussed later.

The two formal methods whereby the Architect could nominate Sub-Contractors under the original 1980 regime have now been withdrawn, following the issue in March 1991 of Amendment 10. As the new provisions are complex, the Contractor should ensure that his staff are re-trained so as to be able to operate the new regime safely.

However, the Contractor should be aware that nomination of Sub-Contractors may occur informally by virtue of Clause 35.1, whereby nomination of Sub-Contractors will occur automatically whenever the Architect has reserved to himself the right of final selection and approval of a Sub-Contractor.

As the Architect cannot nominate a Sub-Contractor against whom the Contractor makes a reasonable objection (Clause 35.5), the first thing that the Contractor should do on receipt of an Architect's

Instruction on Nomination NSC/N, is to consider whether or not he has any such reasonable objection. If he has, he must notify the Architect of his objection within seven days. The Contractor should then note the only alternative instructions which the Architect is empowered to issue if the Contractor makes such a reasonable objection.

If the Contractor has no such reasonable objection, he must contact the Nominated Sub-Contractor and proceed to complete NSC/T Part 3, and execute, and get the Sub-Contractor to execute, Agreement NSC/A, and then send the relevant copies to the Architect (Clause 35.7).

The Contractor should take care in carrying out negotiations with Nominated Sub-Contractors. The two most important matters are:

(a) Special attendances

It is important to establish the precise details of all the special attendances that are required by the Nominated Sub-Contractor, and then to establish whether or not they have either been covered in his tender, or are part of the obligations placed on the Contractor through the Contract Bills.

(b) Programme

It is vital that the Contractor should obtain the Nominated Sub-Contractor's agreement to that part of the Master Programme relating to the Sub-Contract Work. If this cannot be agreed, the Contractor should consider whether the Master Programme can be amended to overcome the problem.

However, any amendment to the Master Programme must take into account the programmes of all other persons who may be affected. If such amendments can be made, copies of the revised Master Programme must be sent to the Architect, and to any other person who has been provided with the original.

If the Contractor cannot reach agreement with the Nominated Sub-Contractor within 10 working days, he will be unable to comply with Clause 35.7, and should then operate the provisions of Clause 35.8, and await the Architect's decision under Clause 35.9.

4. Nominated Suppliers

Where there has been thorough pre-contract preparation, the Architect will be in a position to issue instructions regarding Nominated Suppliers at this stage. It is therefore appropriate to deal with this matter now. The situation where there has not been thorough pre-contract preparation, resulting in nomination instructions being issued post-contract, will be discussed later.

Nominated Suppliers arise in only two ways:

(a) Where the Architect issues an instruction to expend a Prime Cost Sum in favour of a named person (Clauses 36.1.1 and 2).
(b) Where the Architect issues an instruction under either Clause 13.12 or 13.13, in which specified materials or goods are only obtainable from a sole source of supply (Clauses 36.1.3 and 4).

It should be noted that where it is provided in the Contract Bills that the Contractor is to supply and fix materials or goods, the supplier does not become a Nominated Supplier, even if a supplier has been named in the Contract Bills or is a sole supplier of the materials or goods (Clause 36.1.2).

The Contractor should remember that, by virtue of Clause 36.4, the Architect can only validly nominate a supplier who is prepared to enter into a contract of sale with the Contractor which includes the terms set out in Clauses 36.4.1–9. This means that if the supplier nominated by the Architect will not enter into such a contract, the nomination is invalid.

On receipt of an Architect's instruction appointing a Nominated Supplier, the Contractor should immediately contact the supplier to see whether such a contract can be agreed. All parts of Clauses 36.4.1–9 are important, but of over-riding importance from the Contractor's point of view is the programme for delivery of the materials or goods (Clause 36.4.3). It is vital that the Contractor should obtain the Nominated Supplier's agreement to supply the materials or goods as required to enable the Contractor to keep to the Master Programme. If this cannot be agreed, the Contractor should consider whether the Master Programme can be amended to overcome the problem.

However, any amendment to the Master Programme must take into account the programmes of all other persons who may be affected. If such amendments can be made, copies of the revised

Master Programme must be sent to the Architect, and to any other person who has been provided with the original.

If the supplier will not enter into a contract of sale with the Contractor which includes the terms set out in Clauses 36.4.1–9, the Contractor should immediately notify the Architect and explain the reasons why the nomination cannot be accepted. It is then for the Architect to make an alternative nomination, or to suggest ways in which the problem may be overcome, as is envisaged by Clause 36.4.

5. Briefing on-site staff

The Contracts Manager should at this stage consult with those who carried out the basic research on the project, especially as to "pricing the Architect" and the degree to which there has been pre-contract preparation by the Architect. This will be invaluable in planning the management of operations on site.

On-site staff should be instructed as to the importance of maintaining thorough and comprehensive records, of which the Daily Site Diary is the central requirement. This should not provide the perfunctory record which it all too often does. In addition to listing the usual facts, it should also include the following details:

(a) The works in progress throughout the site.
(b) Unforeseen construction difficulties which may occur, especially where these result from design.
(c) The works inspected by, and matters discussed with, official visitors, especially the Architect, Consultants, Clerks of Works, Building Inspectors, etc., especially where it seems that a variation is likely.
(d) Any delaying factors.
(e) Any suspicions that the on-site staff may have that the design is likely to lead to the development of defects – e.g. damp-proof courses in the wrong place. The Contractor has a duty to warn the Architect if he knows, or ought to know, that following the design is likely to lead to the development of defects.
(f) Any discrepancies or divergences between the documents listed in Clause 23.1, which may have been found, or suspected.

These matters should be the subject of daily reports to the Contracts Manager in order that he can decide what action, if any, should be taken.

On-site staff should be instructed never to act on any instructions, especially verbal instructions, whether given by the Architect or others, or to deviate in any way from the Contract Documents until instructions have been sought and obtained from the Contracts Manager.

F Operations on Site

During the carrying out of work on site, the two most important matters from the Contractor's point of view in avoiding claims, or at least putting himself in the most advantageous position if claims cannot be avoided, relate to delays and finance.

1. Delays

The Contractor is under an obligation to complete the Works on or before the Completion Date (Clause 23.1.1) and, if he fails to do so, he will be liable to Damages for non-completion (Clause 24.2.1). It is essential therefore to monitor the Master Programme at least once weekly in order to see that the work is progressing according to plan or, if it is not, to decide what action is necessary. If the deviation from programme is caused by a factor for which he is himself responsible ('culpable delay'), immediate remedial action is necessary. If the deviation from programme is caused by a factor(s) for which he is not responsible ('non-culpable delay'), he would be entitled to have the Completion Date extended under the provisions of Clause 25.

The Contractor is under an obligation to give notice in writing if the progress of the Works is being or is likely to be delayed (Clause 25.2.1.1), and it should be noted that this is irrespective of whether or not a Relevant Event (Clause 25.4) is involved.

The words "or is likely to be delayed" are important because, for instance, the Architect may genuinely not realise that an instruction is likely to cause delay. If the Contractor knows that the instruction is likely to cause delay, and gives due notice, the Architect is given an opportunity to take avoiding action.

Failure by the Contractor to give notice at the proper time is not necessarily fatal to an entitlement to an extension of time. It has been held that in certain circumstances the Architect may be under a duty to grant an extension of time notwithstanding the absence of notice.[22] However, this should only be relied on as a longstop, because the Architect would argue that he did not know that an instruction would cause delay and, if he had been warned by the Contractor, he would have withdrawn or modified the instruction, or issued compensatory instructions – e.g. cancellation of other work – and thus avoided or reduced the delay. In such a case, the length of the extension will almost certainly be less than that to which the Contractor would have been entitled if due notice had been given.

In order to establish his right to, and to deny the Architect an excuse to delay the issue of, an extension of time, the Contractor should meticulously follow the provisions of Clause 25.2 by giving the cause of delay and the Relevant Event (Clause 25.2.1.1); the expected effects (Clause 25.2.2.1); if appropriate, the extent to which the critical path is likely to be affected (Clause 25.2.2.2; and by providing up-dating notices (Clause 25.2.3).

The Contractor should appreciate that Relevant Events fall into three categories, and that each delay must be treated as appropriate to the category involved:

(a) Relevant Events, Clauses 25.4.1, 2, 3, 4, 9, 10 and 11, relate to delays where neither the Architect nor the Employer is responsible. These entitle the Contractor to extensions of time, but not to loss and/or expense under Clause 26.1.
(b) Relevant Events, Clauses 25.4.5, 6, 8, 12 and 13, relate to delays for which either the Architect or the Employer is responsible. These entitle the Contractor to extensions of time and also to loss and/or expense under Clauses 26.1, 26.2 and 34.3.
(c) Relevant Event, Clause 25.4.7 constitutes a special case. It is similar to category (a), in that it entitles the Contractor to an extension of time, but not to loss and/or expense. However, the difference is that the Contractor can recover such loss and/or expense as he incurs from any Nominated Sub-Contractor or Nominated Supplier in culpable delay. In such cases, the Contractor should be careful to follow exactly the relevant provisions of the Main Contract, and the Sub-Contracts, in order to be able to prosecute a successful claim against a defaulter.

It is important for the Contractor to appreciate the position regarding delays caused by Local Authorities or Statutory Under-takers. Relevant Event Clause 25.4.11 only applies where the work was "in pursuance of its statutory obligations". If the work is the result of an agreement between the Employer and the Local Authority or Statutory Undertaker, which is commonly the case, the appropriate Relevant Event is Clause 25.4.8.1. The reason why this is important for the Contractor is because, whereas Relevant Event, Clause 25.4.11 is in category (a), with no entitlement to loss and/or expense, Relevant Event, Clause 25.4.8.1 is in category (b), which does carry an entitlement to loss and/or expense!

It is obviously important to pay careful attention to delays which relate to all Relevant Events, including those in category (a), because extensions of time provide appropriate relief from Damages for non-completion (Clause 24). However, it is even more important to pay careful attention to delays which relate to Relevant Events in categories (b) and (c), because these also entitle the Contractor to loss and/or expense, either from the Employer or from a Nominated Sub-Contractor or Nominated Supplier.

Notices (Clause 25.2.1.1) and applications (Clause 26.1) do not have to be in any particular form provided that they are clear and unambiguous. Examples of suitable letters, together with other typical forms and letters, are to be found in *Contract Documentation for Contractors*.[23]

2. Finance

Normally, Interim Certificates are issued at not less than monthly intervals (Clause 30.1.3), and the Employer is given not less than 14 days in which to make payment (Clauses 30.1.1). The Contractor is therefore always financing the Works for minimum periods of six weeks or more. As has been explained, this creates a weakness for the Contractor in relation to claims, in that he is always a creditor. There are four particular reasons, one obvious, the others not quite so obvious, why the Contractor should do everything possible to restrict the amount of credit:

(a) It minimises the Contractor's overdraft charges.
(b) If the Architect fails to issue a certificate at the proper time, or if an Interim Certificate is not in accordance with the Contract Conditions, the Contractor can immediately go to arbitration before matters get out of hand.
(c) If the Employer fails to make full and prompt payments, or interferes with the issue of any certificate, the Contractor can threaten to determine his employment under the Contract (Clauses 28.1.1 and 2). Such a course would create considerable

problems for the Employer, and would encourage settlement. After Practical Completion, the Employer will have occupied the project, and the Contractor will have lost the benefit of withdrawal from the site as a means of encouraging settlement. As has been explained earlier, the Contractor, as creditor, would then be at a disadvantage in any legal proceedings, and would almost always have to accept, or be awarded, less than his true entitlement.

(d) Keeping up to date with valuations will prove invaluable at Practical Completion. Not only will it keep the amount outstanding to a minimum, it will also leave little to be dealt with in the preparation of the final account – "statement of all adjustments to be made to the Contract Sum" (Clause 30.6.1.2.2), and reduce the delay in issuing the Final Certificate (Clause 30.8).

For these reasons, the Contractor should do all in his power to keep the amount outstanding at Practical Completion to a minimum.

The Contractor should insist that valuations for Interim Certificates are carried out by the Quantity Surveyor, "not more than 7 days before the date of the Interim Certificate", and that they fully accord with the contract provisions. The Contractor should ensure that his surveyor is familiar with all matters which should be taken into account in valuations for Interim Certificates, and which are conveniently listed in Clause 30.2.1. The Contractor should note that not all amounts are subject to retention (Clause 30.2.2).

It is important to ensure that variations and expenditure of Provisional Sums (Clause 13.4) are valued correctly and fully by the Quantity Surveyor at the relevant (usually monthly) intervals.

For obvious reasons, any attempt by the Quantity Surveyor to *only* include provisional valuations should be strenuously resisted. To ensure that there is no excuse for delayed or only partial valuation, the Contractor should promptly submit all information which the Quantity Surveyor will need in order to carry out his valuations, including dayworks sheets, invoices, etc.

It is also important that loss and/or expense (Clauses 26.1 and 34.3.1) should be valued correctly by the Architect or Quantity Surveyor, and certified, as soon as possible after they have been incurred (Clause 3). Unlike notices required by Clause 25.2.1.1, the Contractor is not under a contractual obligation to make applications under Clause 26.1 – he has a right to do so if he chooses.

Failure to make an application at the proper time will be fatal to any claim for loss and/or expense based on Clause 26.1. All will not be lost, however, because it has been held that the Contractor can always make a claim for damages at common law.[24] However, taking this course is far more difficult, the benefits are far less than would have been the case with claims based on Clause 26.1, and recovery will be very much later. It should therefore only be relied on as a longstop, and the Contractor should always make an application to the Architect, under Clause 26.1, if he has incurred or is likely to incur direct loss and/or expense in either of two circumstances:

(a) If possession of the site is deferred where in the Appendix Clause 23.1.2 is made applicable. Where Clause 23.1.2 is not made applicable, deferred possession of the site would create a special case, in respect of which the Contractor should take immediate legal advice.
(b) If the regular progress of the Works has been or is likely to be materially affected by any of the matters referred to in Clause 26.2.

The Contractor should note that application has to be made "as soon as it has become, or should reasonably have become, apparent to him that the regular progress of the Works or any part thereof has been or is likely to be affected" (Clause 26.1.1). For similar reasons to those given regarding Clause 25.2.1.1 notices, the words "or likely to be affected" are important.

The Contractor should also note that loss and/or expense is not necessarily related to delay, even though some Relevant Events (Clause 25.4) are the same as some of the matters referred to in Clause 26.2. For instance, consider the case where the Architect issues an instruction requiring extra work at a time when the Contractor is in a position to achieve early completion. If the Contractor can still complete by the Completion Date, an extension of time will not be necessary, but loss and/or expense will have been incurred due to the Contractor having to remain on site to carry out the additional work.

Unlike notices of delay (Clause 25.2.1.1), no details have to be provided in support of an application made under Clause 26.1, ascertainment being left to the Architect or Quantity Surveyor. However, such details can be requested (Clauses 26.1.2 and 3). Waiting for, and then complying with, such requests will delay the ascertainment and payment of loss and/or expense. To avoid such delays, the Contractor should not wait for a request, but should submit such details as he is able to supply with the application.

Such details should include for the administrative costs of processing Architect's instructions, a matter which is often ignored in valuations under Clause 13.4, and ascertainment under Clauses 26.1. Yet such administrative costs can be very considerable, and can cause serious disruption of, and indeed damage to, other work by off-site staff. Cases have been known where, due to the number and complexity of Architect's Instructions, the contractor has had to engage additional staff to cope with it.

The Contractor should check that Interim Certificates are fully in accordance with valuations (Clause 3).

3. Architect's instructions

The Contractor should take great care in regard to Architect's instructions. Clause 4.3.1 provides that all Architect's instructions shall be in writing, and the Contractor should insist on this being followed in all cases. It follows that under no circumstances should the Contractor act on any oral instruction, and he should never follow the procedure set out in Clause 4.3.2 except, in a rare case, where he stands to benefit from the instruction.

The Contractor should never act on instructions or directions which the Employer, Consultants, Clerks of Works or Building Inspectors may issue, until such instructions or directions have been confirmed, in writing, by the Architect.

The Contractor should make quite sure that he is not by-passed by Nominated Sub-Contractors being given, and acting on, instructions issued to them by Consultants. This is a common practice and can cause enormous problems for the Contractor.

The Architect can only lawfully issue instructions in respect of which he is expressly empowered to issue instructions. On receipt of an instruction, the Contractor should check to see whether it is clear as to which power the Architect is exercising. If an instruction is not clear, the Contractor should request the Architect to specify the power (Clause 4.2). If the Contractor does not agree with the Architect's reply, he should think carefully because, if he does comply with the instruction, the decision given by the Architect cannot be challenged at a later date unless the Contractor has served notice of dispute under Clause 41.

The following commonly occurring Architect's instructions are of special importance, because all have implications in terms of time and cost:

(a) Decisions regarding a discrepancy or divergence between Contract Documents (Clause 2.3).
(b) Variations (Clause 13.2).
(c) Expenditure of Provisional Sums (Clause 13.3).
(d) Postponement (Clause 23.2).
(e) Appointing Nominated Sub-Contractors and Nominated Suppliers (Clauses 35 and 36).

4. Late instructions

As recommended, the Contractor should, in the 'Project Planning' Stage, have given a list of outstanding information to the Architect, and marked the Master Programme with the dates on which each piece of that information is required.

The Contractor should not, however, rely on that as satisfying the requirement to apply for instructions, drawings, details and levels. He should monitor the requirements set out in the Master Programme, and consider whether those dates are still valid, and remind the Architect by making specific requests if outstanding information has not already been provided. Only if this is done will the Contractor be able to sustain a claim for extensions of time (Relevant Event Clause 25.4.6) and loss and/or expense (Clauses 26.1 and 26.2.1) on the basis of late instructions.

Of particular importance is the possibility of late instructions for the appointment of such Nominated Sub-Contractors and Nominated Suppliers as are not appointed at the 'Project Planning' Stage. The advice given in that section above, as to the procedures to be adopted, is of even greater importance at this stage, because the loss and/or expense which would be incurred by any delay in the 'Project Planning' Stage would be far less than would be incurred by delay occurring when the contract is in full flow.

Circumstances may arise whereby re-nomination becomes necessary, as provided by Clause 35.24. When the Architect makes a further nomination, the Contractor should go through exactly the same procedure as recommended above, but with even greater care.

Under Clause 5.4, the Architect is under a duty to issue such further drawings or details as are reasonably necessary to explain or amplify the Contract Drawings. This may lead to unfortunate problems because there may be a genuine difference of opinion as to what further drawings or details are reasonably necessary.

It sometimes happens that the Architect genuinely thinks that he has provided all the information that the Contractor will require, whereas the Contractor may think that further drawings or details will be forthcoming. Such an unfortunate 'falling between stools' can be prevented if the Contractor considers well ahead and tells the Architect in good time what further drawings or details he will require.

5. Management supervision

The Contracts Manager should appreciate that on-site staff are subject to many pressures and can become overwhelmed by day-to-day problems to the detriment of forward planning. He should therefore, in addition to supervising off-site staff, also monitor on-site activities, consider future requirements, and give support to on-site staff. He should also check to see that all contract provisions are being complied with.

Friction can often arise between on-site staff and other persons connected with the Works, of whom there are many, including architectural assistants, Clerks of Works, Consultants, Employer's representatives, Nominated and Domestic Sub-Contractors, Building Inspectors, etc. The Contracts Manager should monitor such situations and take such action as is necessary to prevent such friction adversely affecting the work.

Quality control is a most important function on all contracts. Contractors are not entitled to have this service performed for them by others, to their quite justified annoyance, as is all too often the case. Contractors should therefore appoint a member of their off-site staff to exercise quality control, and his task should be to check the work as it progresses, and to ensure that any deficiencies are corrected promptly and efficiently.

6. Meetings

Meetings can be dangerous, especially site meetings called by the Architect. The Contractor should insist on an agenda being provided, in order that the relevant matters may be properly considered in advance of the meeting, and that appropriate staff may be delegated to attend. Detailed notes should be taken, and submitted to the Contracts Manager, of all matters which are discussed and, more importantly, all decisions which are taken, in order that he may decide what action, if any, should be taken. These notes should be compared with the minutes when these are issued, and the Contracts Manager should immediately challenge any minute with which he disagrees.

Particular care should be taken if the Architect is one of those who calls regular site meetings:

(a) The Contractor will be asked to provide monthly reports for presentation to, and consideration at, those meetings. Such reports should be prepared with care because they will become part of the written record.
(b) If, as is usually the case, other reports will be considered at such meetings, the Contractor should ask for these to be provided seven days in advance so that they may be considered and commented upon at the meeting. If such other reports are not provided in advance, the Contractor should reserve his right to make post-meeting comments for inclusion in the minutes.

7. Records

The value of maintaining thorough and comprehensive written records cannot possibly be overstated. Knowledge that such records exist can often deter a potential opponent from taking action. If, however, the Contractor does get involved in legal proceedings, such records will prove to be absolutely invaluable.

In addition to contractual records, dated notes of all telephone calls and meetings should be kept, and all but trivial matters should be confirmed in writing.

A photographic record should be kept, to illustrate:

(a) The state of the Works and progress, which should be taken at least at weekly intervals.
(b) Any constructional difficulties as may occur.
(c) Any work which has been condemned or criticised by the Architect, Consultants, Clerks of Works, Building Inspectors, etc.

(d) Any parts of the design of the Works which it is suspected are likely to prove defective, and about which the Architect has been warned.

The photographs should be taken with a camera which automatically records the date on the film. However, since it will be known that the dating mechanism can be altered, each batch of prints should also be signed and date-stamped by the processor.

G Completion

A frequent, and often justifiable, complaint against contractors is a failure to bring the project to a proper state of completion. Such complaints are exacerbated when a project is presented for hand-over in an incomplete or defective state and the Contractor expects a 'snagging list' to be provided by the Clerk of Works and/or the Architect – neither of whom are under any obligation to provide, or paid for performing, what is in fact a quality control service on behalf of the Contractor.

This situation is a common cause of delay in the issue of the Certificate of Practical Completion, and leads to the development of a dispute, or adds fuel to an already existing dispute, and this will cause a serious weakening of the Contractor's position.

To avoid such problems, the person appointed by the Contractor to exercise quality control should identify any incomplete or defective items, and ensure that these are corrected promptly and efficiently. No project should be presented for hand-over until he is satisfied that it has been properly completed and is free of defects.

The Contractor should ensure that all mechanical services are tested, commissioned and approved by the Architect, the appropriate Consultant and, where relevant, the appropriate public authority.

The person exercising quality control should attend the hand-over meeting and, if that results in a 'snagging list' being issued, he should ensure that any justified items are attended to promptly and efficiently.

Prompt and efficient hand-over not only avoids, or reduces, the Contractor's liability for Damages for non-completion, it also ensures early release of the first moiety of retention (Clause 30.4.1.3).

H Defects Liability Period

Immediately following Practical Completion, the Contractor should chase and provide all outstanding documents which will be required by the Quantity Surveyor in his work of preparing the 'final account' – more properly the "statement of all adjustments to be made to the Contract Sum" (Clause 30.6.1.2.2) – including dayworks sheets, invoices, etc. The sooner these documents are provided the better, because it will remove non-provision as an excuse for delay in the preparation of the 'final account', and will also remove one of the reasons for delay in issuing the Final Certificate (Clause 30.8).

The Contractor should not wait until all outstanding documents are available. He should provide them piecemeal as they come to hand, because he is entitled to Interim Certificates after Practical Completion "as and when further amounts are ascertained as payable to the Contractor from the Employer" (Clause 30.1.3), and this reduces yet further the amount outstanding.

During the Defects Liability Period, the Architect has the power to issue instructions for the making good of "any defect, shrinkage or other fault which may appear" and which requires immediate attention (Clause 17.3). These should be dealt with promptly by the Contractor in order to avoid, or reduce, consequential damage, for which he would be held liable.

It should be noted, however, that, as an alternative to issuing an instruction for the making good of such a defect, Clause 17.3 empowers the Architect to make an appropriate deduction from the Contract Sum. If the Architect adopts this course, the Contractor should check the validity of the alleged defect, and also the amount which the Architect proposes to deduct.

J Feedback

At the end of the Defects Liability Period, the Architect has the power to issue a schedule of defects. The person exercising quality control should immediately inspect all the items on the schedule to see that all are valid and, if so, the Contractor should ensure that prompt attention is given to the necessary remedial work, so as to remove the second of the reasons for delay in issuing the Final Certificate (Clause 30.8).

Again it should be noted that, as an alternative to issuing an instruction for the making good of defects, Clause 17.2 empowers the Architect to make an appropriate deduction from the Contract Sum. If the Architect adopts this course, the Contractor should check the validity of the alleged defects, and also the amounts which the Architect proposes to deduct.

Care should be taken when considering the schedule of defects, because it is not unknown for items to be included which are not defects but which constitute variations. These should be challenged.

The Architect is not empowered to issue variation instructions after Practical Completion so, if the Architect asks the Contractor to carry out the work, he can either decline or set his own terms.

It is important that the Contractor should do all that is necessary to achieve early issue of the Final Certificate. Not only will this result in payment of the final balance and the release of the second moiety of retention, it also has considerable legal benefits (Clause 30.9.).

If the Final Certificate is issued in a sum with which the Contractor disagrees, he must invoke the arbitration provisions by serving notice of dispute in accordance with Clause 41.1 within 28 days (Clause 30.9.3). If the Contractor fails to do so, the Final Certificate will become conclusive and the Contractor will be without a remedy (Clause 30.9.1).

The manner of issuing, and the contents of, a notice of dispute is of crucial importance, about which legal advice should always be sought.

All the papers arising in the course of the project should be sorted, all duplicates and other non-essential papers should be discarded, and the remainder should be preserved for at least 10 years.

The Contracts Manager should carefully consider all that has occurred, from the original enquiry to the end of the contract, in order to see what lessons are to be learned from the experience gained.

Conclusion

The vast majority of claims result from disputes between the Contractor and the Architect and/or the Quantity Surveyor. All too often, the first indication that the Employer has of such disputes is when the Contractor invokes the arbitration provisions, by which time matters may have gone beyond the point where formal proceedings can be avoided or disputes compromised.

Contractors think that they must only deal with the Architect and the Quantity Surveyor. This is not a rule, but only a convention. Contractors should appreciate that the Architect and Quantity Surveyor are not parties to the Contract, but only officials. The parties to the Contract are the Employer and the Contractor, and it is their interests which are at stake when disputes cannot be resolved.

Contractors should also appreciate that the reason why they are unable to obtain satisfaction of their claims from the Architect and/ or the Quantity Surveyor is often because one (or other or both) of them is responsible for the claim being made and is trying to protect himself against a possible negligence claim by his client – the Employer.

At the commencement of the Contract, the Contractor should establish direct lines of communication and good relations with the Employer or his appointed representative. Then, when disputes arise which cannot be resolved with the contract officials, the Contractor should not hesitate to approach the Employer direct to make him aware of the situation.

If the Employer is sensible, he will be only too pleased that he has been given the opportunity to intervene before matters get out of hand and his interests are irreparably compromised.

References

1 JCT80, Clause 30.1.1.1.
2 *Hudson's Building and Engineering Contracts*, I.N. Duncan Wallace QC MA, 10th Edition, 1970, London: Sweet & Maxwell, page 860.
3 ibid, page 856.
4 'The Placing and Management of Building Contracts', Report of the Central Council for Works and Buildings, London: HMSO, 1944, Section 37, page 16.
5 Code of Procedure for Single Stage Selective Tendering 1989, National Joint Consultative Committee for Building, London: RIBA Publications Limited.

6 ibid, Section 4.4, and Appendix A.1.

7 'The Placing and Management of Contracts for Building and Civil Engineering Work', Ministry of Public Buildings and Works, London: HMSO, 1964, Section 4.1, page 13.

8 *Action on the Banwell Report*, National Economic Development Office, London: HMSO, 1967, Section 3, pages 7–9.

9 Published paper: "The Contractor! Poor Devil!", Eric W. Seagrove FIOB FFB (Director, Y.J. Lovell (Holdings) Limited), 1973, the Faculty of Building.

10 *Action on the Banwell Report*, National Economic Development Office, London: HMSO, 1967, Section 9.2, page 20.

11 Code of Procedure for Single Stage Selective Tendering 1989, National Joint Consultative Committee for Building, London: RIBA Publications Limited, Section 4.1.3 page 2.

12 ibid, Sections 4.2 – 4.5, pages 3/4.

13 ibid, Section 4.1.3, pages 2/3.

14 'The Placing and Management of Building Contracts', Report of the Central Council for Works and Buildings, London: HMSO, 1944, Section 24, page 10.

15 ibid, Section 26, page 11.

16 Code of Procedure for Single Stage Selective Tendering 1989, National Joint Consultative Committee for Building, London: RIBA Publications Limited, Appendix B.

17 Standard Method of Measurement 7, General Rules 10.1, 10.2, 10.5 and 10.6, and Amendments to JCT80, resulting from Amendment 7, July 1988.

18 Code of Procedure for Single Stage Selective Tendering 1989, National Joint Consultative Committee for Building, London: RIBA Publications Limited, Section 5.2.

19 ibid, Section 6.2, page 4.

20 ibid, Sections 6.3 and 6.4, page 4.

21 *London Borough of Merton* v *Stanley Hugh Leach Limited* [1985] 32 BLR 51.

22 ibid.

23 *Contract Documentation for Contractors*, 1985, Vincent Powell-Smith LLM DLitt FCIArb, and John Sims FRICS FCIArb, London: Collins.

24 *London Borough of Merton* v *Stanley Hugh Leach Limited* [1985] 32 BLR 51.

4

Sub-Contractors

Prior to studying this chapter, sub-contractors should read Chapter 3 – Contractors – because many of the matters dealt with there apply with even greater force, especially the introduction passages.

As with contractors, sub-contractors also work on a credit basis, providing materials, goods and services for a period before they are paid and, by thus financing operations, are always creditors. However, sub-contractors are even more vulnerable than contractors in respect of claims because they have one more potential 'enemy' – the Contractor – and are one stage further removed from the source of payment. It follows that sub-contractors should be even more careful than contractors to avoid or reduce the incidence of claims.

Furthermore, it is a well-known fact that when a contractor is in trouble, he will attempt to transfer the blame for his defaults on to one of the sub-contractors. It is equally well known that, in doing so, the contractor will pick on what he considers to be the weakest. Sub-contractors should be careful to protect themselves against being made the scapegoat for contractors.

There are two types of Sub-Contractors:

1. Domestic Sub-Contractors are those who are selected and engaged directly by the Contractor.
2. Nominated Sub-Contractors are those who are selected and nominated by the Architect and who the Contractor is obliged to engage whether he likes it or not.

A Dealing with enquiries – Domestic Sub-Contractors

Domestic Sub-Contractors have an advantage over Nominated Sub-Contractors in that their rights and interests cannot be affected by anyone other than the Contractor. However, they have a disadvantage in that they cannot appeal to the Architect in the event of disputes arising which they cannot resolve with the Contractor. Furthermore, they cannot require direct payments to be made by the Employer in the event of the Contractor failing to pay, for whatever reason.

The first thing that a firm or company should do, on receiving an enquiry which could result in a Domestic Sub-Contract, is to 'price the Contractor'. This entails checking not only the enquiring Contractor's track record, but also his financial standing.

As regards the Contractor's track record, the questions to which the research should be addressed include: does the Contractor have a reputation for:

1. Making prompt payments when due?
2. Giving further and/or variation instructions in writing and at reasonable times?
3. Playing fair with Sub-Contractors?

If the answer to any of these questions is in the negative, the tenderer should foresee trouble and anticipate major problems. However, even if the answers to these questions are in the affirmative, it is also important to consider:

1. Whether or not the Contractor is offering to enter into a Sub-Contract on form DOM/1?

   (a) If Sub-Contract DOM/1 is to be used, all 14 Parts of the Appendix should be considered with care, especially Part 4 regarding programming of the Sub-Contract Works. The section of Part 7, relating to Clause 25.5.2, is important in relation to the early release of retention – see that part in parentheses Clause 25.5.2. Part 1 is also important, because Clause 5 of DOM/1 exposes Sub-Contractors to Main Contract liabilities.
   (b) If Sub-Contract DOM/1 is not to be used, expert advice should be sought as to the terms and implications of the Sub-Contract which the Contractor is offering.

2. Whatever form of sub-contract is to be used, it is essential that the tenderer should consider the details of the proposed Sub-Contract Works provided with the enquiry, to ensure that they are sufficiently explicit and not likely to be subject to dispute.
3. The extent to which the Sub-Contract Works will have to be dovetailed into works to be carried out by the Contractor and/or other Sub-Contractors.
4. The programme details with which the successful tenderer will be required to comply.

Another disadvantage which Domestic Sub-Contractors have over Nominated Sub-Contractors is that if their tender (estimate or quotation) is accepted, they will be bound in contract, and cannot then either correct estimating errors or withdraw. Tenders should therefore be very carefully double-checked before submission, not only as to pricing, but also as to any programming details with which they will be required to comply.

For the same reason, and because their circumstances may well change with the passage of time, a tenderer should always state a period within which the tender is to be held open for acceptance.

B Dealing with enquiries – Nominated Sub-Contractors

Nominated Sub-Contractors have a disadvantage as against Domestic Sub-Contractors, in that their rights and interests can be affected by other persons in addition to the Contractor – Architect, Quantity Surveyor and Consultants. However, they have the advantage of being able to exercise rights conferred on them under the Main Contract, if disputes arise which they cannot resolve with the Contractor, Architect or Quantity Surveyor.

Whilst tenderers should take care in the preparation of their tenders, they should remember that, as will be explained, they cannot be bound in contract without being given an opportunity to reconsider and, if appropriate, to withdraw their tender.

Sub-Contractors should know that the two formal methods whereby the Architect could nominate Sub-Contractors under the original 1980 regime have now been withdrawn as a result of the issue in March 1991 of Amendment 10. As the new provisions are complex, and all the related forms are new, tenderers should ensure that their staffs attend re-training courses, and heed advice received from their representative body and independent commentators, so as to be able to operate the new regime properly and with a reasonable degree of safety. The new procedure as it affects Nominated Sub-Contractors is set out on page 16 of Amendment 10.

1. Invitation to Tender NSC/T Part 1

The first thing that a firm or company should do, on receiving an Invitation, is to 'price' the Architect and Quantity Surveyor by the technique explained in Chapter 3 – Contractors. If the Sub-Contract Works have been designed, and will in due course be supervised, by a Consultant, his track record should also be checked.

They should also 'price' the Contractor by the technique explained above under Domestic Sub-Contractors. However, it may be that the enquiry is made before the Contractor has been selected, in which case, tenderers should make a file-note as a reminder to 'price' the Contractor if and when their tender is accepted.

The Invitation comprises nine pages, all with helpful marginal notes, and is divided into five sections:

(a) Page 1 is simply an explanation of abbreviations.
(b) Page 2 comprises the actual invitation. It gives particulars of the required works, gives details of the manner in which tenders are to be submitted, and refers to the tender documents which are provided with the Invitation: "drawings/specifications/bills of quantities/ schedule of rates".

It goes without saying that tenderers should check these documents carefully, but it may not be quite so obvious that they should keep copies, in order that they can be checked with those which will be incorporated into a Sub-Contract.
(c) Page 3 gives details of the Main Contract and its location. It also gives details of the Employer, the contractual officers, other members of the design team, and details of the Contractor if known at that stage. This will be helpful in the 'pricing' referred to earlier.
(d) Pages 4 and 5 are divided into sections 1–11, and these give details of the Main Contract. A copy of the Appendix to the Main Contract is attached, and this should be considered with care. Section 5 gives tenderers the right to inspect the Main Contract Documents, and tenderers would be wise to take

advantage of this, not only for familiarisation purposes, but also because the Nominated Sub-Contract Conditions NSC/C, which will apply, expose Nominated Sub-Contractors to Main Contract liabilities, and other Clauses provide them with Main Contract rights.

(e) The remaining pages, 7–9, are divided into sections 12–17, and these give Sub-Contract Information, all of which should be carefully considered prior to submitting a tender.

2. Employer/Nominated Sub-Contractor Agreement NSC/W

This Agreement will be sent with the Invitation to Tender NSC/T Part 1 and, in order that the tender can be considered, the tenderer must execute this document and return it with the tender. NSC/W replaces NSC/2, and brings both liabilities and benefits. It should be studied with care and, if any doubt exists as to its implications, tenderers should seek advice from their solicitors and, where design services are involved, their insurance brokers should be consulted.

A Nominated Sub-Contractor's principal liabilities arise under the following Clauses:

(a) Clause 2.1. Where the work to be undertaken involves design, selection of materials and/or goods, or satisfaction of performance specifications.

(b) Clause 3.2. Where the Sub-Contractor is to provide information, and defaults in respect of that requirement.

(c) Clause 3.3. If the Sub-Contractor goes into default or causes the Contractor to become entitled to an extension of time by reason of Relevant Event in Clause 25.4.7 of the Main Contract.

(d) Clause 6. In the event of the Sub-Contractor being responsible for the Architect having to re-nominate under Clause 35.24 of the Main Contract.

The principal benefits for the Sub-Contractor are those relating to payment:

(a) Clause 5.1 ensures that the Sub-Contractor will be entitled to early final payment under Clauses 35.17 to 35.19 of the Main Contract. This would be of particular value to those Sub-Contractors whose work will be carried out and completed early in the project.

(b) Clause 7.1 provides that the Employer will pay the Sub-Contractor if the Contractor defaults in making payments certified for payment to the Sub-Contractor.

In the opening paragraphs of this chapter, it was explained that Sub-Contractors are even more vulnerable than Contractors in respect of claims and dispute resolution. And, as explained in the Introduction, the difficulties for a claimant involved in arbitration proceedings, which a Sub-Contractor is most likely to be, have been made far worse by the passing of the Arbitration Act 1979. Therefore a Sub-Contractor should do his utmost to persuade the Employer that Clause 11.5, and the words "Subject to clause 11.5" in Clause 11.4, should be deleted.

3. Tender NSC/T Part 2

The form of Tender comprises eight pages, all with helpful marginal notes, and is divided into three separate sections:

(a) Page 1 is simply an explanation of abbreviations used throughout the document.
(b) Page 2 comprises the actual tender, and pages 3–7 provide the conditions which are to be applicable to the Sub-Contract. As the majority of the content of these pages consist of technical material, it is not thought that tenderers will require any advice from the author, apart from the suggestion that it should all be considered carefully.

   However, tenderers should pay special attention to section 1 on page 6, because it deals with programming and requires tenderers to give periods for both lead-in and execution of work on site. Whilst negotiations will take place at a later date between the successful tenderer and the Contractor regarding programming, care should be taken at this stage so as to avoid creating unnecessary negotiating difficulties.
(c) Page 8, which is divided into sections 1–4, sets out Stipulations which tenderers attach to their tenders. Stipulation 1 is self-explanatory. Stipulation 2 sets out the two bases on which a tender may be withdrawn. Stipulation 3 is important because it gives tenderers the opportunity to insert the period within which they will hold the tender open for acceptance. Because circumstances may well change with the passage of time, tenderers should be careful when stipulating this period.

By Stipulation 4, tenderers acknowledge that if a tender is withdrawn, they will only be paid for any work pre-ordered under an Employer/Nominated Sub-Contractor Agreement NSC/W.

When completing their tender Sub-Contractors would do well to consider which of two situations are involved, and which have to be allowed for:

(a) Where the Sub-Contract Works do not entail the successful tenderer having to provide design services or production drawings, tenderers should consider the degree of preparedness of the Sub-Contract Works, in order to assess the likelihood of delays, disruptions and variations.
(b) Where the Sub-Contract Works do entail the successful tenderer having to provide design services and/or production drawings, tenderers should be especially careful in completing section 1 on page 6 of Tender NSC/T Part 2, relating to the Sub-Contract programme.

C Dealing with enquiries – General

Having done the basic research, a tenderer will know if there are any reasons from the legal, technical, managerial and current workload aspects whether or not the Invitation should be accepted, and must decide on how to respond to the Invitation to tender. If the indications are unfavourable, he may decline to tender, or he may decide to tender, but to add a percentage to cover such non-recoverable damage which he might suffer.

However, economic and/or political circumstances may dictate that a tender should be submitted, despite unfavourable indications. In such a case, the tenderer should be aware that he will have to provide efficient management procedures to eliminate, or at least reduce, the risk of suffering non-recoverable damage.

D Formation of Sub-Contract – Domestic Sub-Contractors

Two matters should be checked immediately on receipt of an order from the Contractor:

1. If the period which the tenderer had stipulated within which the tender was open for acceptance has expired, the order would not constitute 'Acceptance' and a legally binding Sub-Contract would not have been concluded. It would then be open to the tenderer to negotiate revised terms with the Contractor.
2. The tenderer should carefully check that the Contractor's order, and any documents sent therewith, are identical in every respect with the tender which he submitted in response to the Contractor's invitation. If they are identical, the Contractor's order would constitute 'Acceptance' and a legally binding Sub-Contract would have been concluded.

   However, if there are differences, the Contractor's order would not constitute 'Acceptance' – but would rank as a counter-offer which the recipient would not be obliged to accept. Especially where differences are significant, the tenderer must immediately draw these to the Contractor's attention, and a revised tender should be submitted.

In either case, if the tenderer were to act on the Contractor's order he would be deemed to have waived his right to object to the order being placed out of time or under different terms, and a legally binding Sub-Contract would have been concluded, and he would be unable to claim additional money or time at a later date.

E Formation of Sub-Contract – Nominated Sub-Contractors

When the Architect has selected the Sub-Contractor that he intends to nominate, he will send a Nominated Instruction NSC/N to the Contractor, and will send a copy to the successful tenderer.

The Architect cannot nominate a Sub-Contractor against whom the Contractor makes a reasonable objection. If the Contractor has such a reasonable objection he will notify the Architect, and no Sub-Contract can result. If the Contractor has no such reasonable objection, he will contact the successful tenderer in order to settle the terms of a Sub-Contract by completing the Particular Conditions NSC/T Part 3.

As indicated earlier, the submission of a Tender NSC/T Part 2 does not bind the successful tenderer to enter into a Sub-Contract. A Tender can be withdrawn by notice in writing to the Employer if the name of the Contractor was not known at the time of tendering (Agreement NSC/W Clause 1.2 and Tender NSC/T Part 2 Stipulation 2). A Tender is automatically withdrawn if the Architect fails to issue Nominated Instruction NSC/N within the period set by the tenderer (Tender NSC/T Part 2 Stipulation 3).

If the tender is not withdrawn, the successful tenderer is obliged to negotiate with the Contractor in order to settle the terms of a Sub-Contract by completing the Particular Conditions NSC/T Part 3. All parts are important, but the greatest care must be taken with section 1 on page 2, regarding programming. If there has been a delay between the submission of a tender, as often happens, the tenderer should consider whether he can still comply with the programme which he set out in section 1, on page 6, of his Tender NSC/T Part 2.

Only if the successful tenderer is satisfied on all matters should he signify his agreement by appending his signature where provided on page 4 of NSC/T Part 3. If he is unable to agree to any part of NSC/T Part 3, he must notify the Contractor in writing of the reasons, and then await further instructions. This could result in further negotiations with the Contractor, but the Architect could exercise his right to choose another sub-contractor or even to omit the sub-contract work.

If the successful tenderer has reached agreement with the Contractor, the next step would be for him and the Contractor to execute the Articles of Nominated Sub-Contractor Agreement NSC/A. This is a crucial stage because once the tenderer has executed NSC/A, he will be bound in contract in accordance with its terms. It is very difficult, if not impossible, for any errors to be corrected.

It is assumed that the successful tenderer has studied and understood the implications of the sub-contract documents as advised earlier. However, the documents are for general application, but the successful tenderer is now required to execute an NSC/A which particularises this sub-contract. The details should therefore be checked with care to ensure that they are identical with the terms of his tender, or with any amendments to which he has agreed subsequently.

Of special importance in this connection are:

1. The Fifth Recital to NSC/A.
2. All three sections of Article 1 to NSC/A.

3. The "Numbered Documents annexed hereto", as referred to in Article 1, Section 1.1 of NSC/A.
4. Article 3.

If there are differences between what is presented and what was agreed, the tenderer should not execute NSC/A until these differences have been corrected.

F Sub-Contract period and Operations on Site

If the recommendations relating to pre-contract procedures have been followed, the Sub-Contractor will have done everything possible for the Sub-Contract to start on the right foot. However, it is in this period that claims and disputes commonly occur, so consideration must now be given as to the manner in which Sub-Contractors should perform in order to reduce the likelihood of having to make claims, or having claims made against them.

During this period, the most important matters from a Sub-Contractor's point of view, in relation to claims, relate to delays, disruptions and finance.

1. Delays and/or disruption

Under this heading two situations have to be considered:

(a) Case 1

This case comprises those Sub-Contracts where the Works are of an entire nature on a single structure and where the Works do not have to be co-ordinated with, or dovetailed into, Works by the Contractor or other Sub-Contractors. In other words, where the Sub-Contractor enters upon the site, carries out his work as one continuous operation, and without interference by others. For example, piling, other foundations or a steel frame for a simple office block.

(b) Case 2

This case comprises those Sub-Contracts where the Works are to be carried out in stages on a number of separate units or phases, and where the Works do have to be co-ordinated with, and dovetailed into, Works by the Contractor or other Sub-Contractors. The most extreme examples are electrical, mechanical or plumbing installations, involving first and second fixing, on a series of independent housing units.

The practical and managerial problems under Case 1 are as nothing by comparison with those under Case 2. Similarly, the likelihood of disputes, claims and counter-claims in respect of delays and disruption are much greater with Case 2 than with Case 1. Therefore, whilst the following recommendations will apply to all Sub-Contractors, they are obviously of the greatest importance for Case 2 Sub-Contractors.

Sub-Contractor claims relating to delay occur where there has been delay for which the Sub-Contractor was not responsible ('non-culpable delay'), and this has resulted in the Sub-Contractor being unable to complete his work by the Completion Date (or Dates for a phased contract). Such claims will be for the Completion Date (or Dates) to be extended. (DOM/1 Clause 11.2, and NSC/C Clauses 2.2 to 2.7 incl.) In most cases, the Sub-Contractor's claim will also be for direct loss and/or expense. (DOM/1 Clauses 13.1 and 13.2, and NSC/C Clauses 4.38 and 4.39 incl.)

It frequently occurs that there will be interference with the Sub-Contractor's work by others, but which does not result in his being unable to complete his work by the Completion Date (or Dates). The Sub-Contractor's claim will then only be for direct loss and/or expense for what is termed 'disruption'.

Claims (or Counter-claims) against a Sub-Contractor may also be in two parts:

(a) All Sub-Contractors will be under an obligation to complete the Sub-Contract Works on or before the Completion Date (or Dates). If they fail to do so ('culpable delay'), they will be liable for such loss and damage as has been incurred by the Contractor. (DOM/1 Clauses 11.1 and 12 and NSC/C Clause 4.40.)

Furthermore, a Nominated Sub-Contractor who has executed an Employer/Nominated Sub-Contractor Agreement NSC/W would be liable for losses suffered by the Employer.

(b) A Sub-Contractor would also be liable for any direct loss and/or expense which the Contractor incurs as a result of any act, omission or default of the Sub-Contractor which results in the regular progress of the Works being materially affected, even if it did not cause the Contractor to be unable to complete the Works by the Main Contract Completion Date.

As has been explained in the preamble to this chapter, Sub-Contractors are even more vulnerable than Contractors in respect of claims. Two courses of action are therefore essential. They should:

(a) Make sure that the Sub-Contract Manager fully understands the Sub-Contract Clauses referred to above, and also appreciates the appropriate action which must be taken when circumstances dictate.
(b) Monitor the programme agreed with the Contractor on at least a weekly basis, in order to see whether or not that programme is being met and, if it is not, to decide what action should be taken.

If the deviation from programme is caused by a factor for which the Sub-Contractor is himself responsible (culpable delay), it is essential that appropriate remedial action is taken immediately. If this is not done, the Sub-Contractor will run the risk of becoming liable for damages, and giving the Contractor or other Sub-Contractors an excuse for their own delays. In this connection, Sub-Contractors should be 'whiter than white'.

However, if the deviation from programme is caused by a factor for which the Sub-Contractor is not responsible (non-culpable delay), he will be entitled to have the Completion Date extended, provided the delay is caused by the Contractor or by one of the Relevant Events set out in Clause 11.10 of DOM/1, and Clause 2.6 of NSC/C, as appropriate.

Sub-Contractors should appreciate that Relevant Events fall into two categories, and that each delay must be treated as appropriate to the category involved:

(a) Category 1 Relevant Events comprise Sub-Clauses 1, 2, 3, 4, 7, 9, 10 and 11, and relate to delays where neither the Contractor, Architect or Employer is responsible. Whilst these entitle Sub-Contractors to have the Completion Date extended, they do not entitle them to loss and/or expense.
(b) Category 2 Relevant Events comprise Sub-Clauses 5, 6, 8, 12, 13, 14 and 15, and relate to delays for which the Contractor, Architect or Employer is responsible. Delays in this category not only entitle the Sub-Contractor to have the Completion Date extended, they also entitle him to loss and/or expense.

In order to secure his entitlement to have the Completion Date (Dates) extended, the Sub-Contractor must immediately serve written notice on the Contractor as required by DOM/1 Clause 11.2.1 or in the Sub-Contracts here considered (DOM/1 and NSC/C) and, in order to secure his entitlement to loss and/or expense where appropriate, the Sub-Contractor must immediately make written application to the Contractor as required by DOM/1 Clause 13.1 or NSC/C Clauses 4.38.1 or 4.39.

Notices and applications do not have to be in any particular form provided that they are clear and unambiguous. Examples of suitable letters, together with other typical forms and letters, are to be found in *Contract Documentation for Contractors* – see reference 23 to Chapter 3 – Contractors.

2. Finance

In relation to the Sub-Contracts here considered (DOM/1 and NSC/C), payments will normally become due at not less than monthly periods, and the Contractor will have 17 days from the due date within which to make payment. Sub-Contractors are therefore always financing the Works for periods of six weeks or more. As has been explained, this creates a weakness for Sub-Contractors in relation to claims, in that they are always creditors.

As has also been explained in Chapter 3 – Contractors, there are particular reasons why a contractor should do everything possible to restrict the amount of credit to a minimum. Because Sub-Contractors are more vulnerable than Contractors, it is even more necessary for them to keep tight credit control.

It is essential for the member of the Sub-Contractor's staff who is to be responsible for credit control to fully understand the provisions relating to finance in the relevant Sub-Contract, and the contractual procedures which must be followed in order to protect the Sub-Contractor's reasonable interests.

(a) Domestic Sub-Contractors

Under DOM/1, the provisions relating to payment are set out in Clause 21.

The first interim payment is due within one month after the commencement of the Sub-Contract Works on site (Clause 21.2.1). There will be cases where the Sub-Contractor will be required to carry out works off-site prior to commencing on-site works. Where these off-site works are extensive, the Sub-Contractor should note the alternative for an agreement to be made with the Contractor that the first payment will be due within one month from commencement of the off-site works. Subsequent interim payments will be due at intervals not exceeding one month calculated from the date when the first payment was due.

Whilst the Sub-Contract does not specifically require it, the Sub-Contractor should make written applications for interim payments, and to do so promptly. Full details as to how the amount of the application is computed should be provided, in order to prevent delay which could result from the Contractor exercising the right conferred on him by Clause 21.4.4.

(b) Nominated Sub-Contractors

Under NSC/C, the provisions relating to interim payments are set out in Clauses 4.14 to 4.22. Payments will be made by the Contractor on the basis of Directions which he receives from the Architect. The Architect is required to include amounts due to Nominated Sub-Contractors in his Interim Certificates which will normally be issued at monthly intervals. The date on which the first interim payment will be due to the Sub-Contractor will depend on the point in the monthly cycle when the Sub-Contract Works were commenced. Subsequent interim payments will be due at monthly intervals.

It is the Architect's (or Quantity Surveyor's) duty to value the Sub-Contract Works in order to arrive at the amount which he will direct the Contractor to pay to the Sub-Contractor. However, to make sure that all relevant matters will be considered by the Architect (or Quantity Surveyor) it is desirable that the Sub-Contractor should make a detailed application to the Contractor with a request that it be forwarded to the Architect. The right to take this course is provided by NSC/C Clauses 4.15.1 and 4.15.2.

Valuations for Interim Certificates are to be made on a date "not more than 7 days before the date of the Interim Certificate" (Main Contract Clause 30.2). Sub-Contractors should therefore ascertain the dates on which the valuations will be carried out, and to ensure that applications are delivered in time for these to be considered.

(c) General

Applications for payment should be prepared with great care, and Sub-Contractors should ensure that their surveyors are familiar with all provisions in the relevant Sub-Contract relating to the making of valuations.

In addition to the value of works executed and materials on site, particular care should be taken to ensure that variations and expenditure of Provisional and Prime Cost Sums are correctly, and fully, valued.

In preparing valuations, it should be noted that DOM/1 Clause 3 and NSC/C Clause 41.1 provide that any amounts to be added to the Sub-Contract Sum must be taken into account in the computation of the interim payment next following. Sub-Contractors should, when making their valuations, make sure that no such amount is left to the final account stage.

Particular care should be taken as Practical Completion of the Sub-Contract Works approaches. Whilst Interim payments can be made, or Interim Certificates issued, after Practical Completion, it is highly desirable that the Sub-Contract accounts and applications should be as up to date as possible when the Practical Completion occurs.

Sub-Contractors should make themselves fully conversant with their rights if payments are not made at the proper time, or in incorrect amounts. In such cases, Sub-Contractors should take the appropriate action immediately. They should never allow matters to drift, because, as has been explained, it is essential that they should maintain tight credit control.

3. Contractor's Directions and Architect's Instructions

Under the Sub-Contracts here considered the Contractor is entitled to issue Directions to a Sub-Contractor, and is obliged to issue Directions resulting from an Architect's Instruction. Such Directions may involve the carrying out of a variation to the Sub-Contract Works. Such Directions are a common cause of difficulty and dispute. Sub-Contractors should therefore take great care in this regard, and should make sure that their site staff will not act on any Direction without having referred the matter to, and obtained approval from, their head office.

The following matters are important:

(a) The Sub-Contractor is only obliged to carry out the Contractor's Directions if they are reasonable. If they are not, the Sub-Contractor should not hesitate to exercise his right to object.

(b) The Contractor's Directions must be in writing, and Sub-Contractors should not carry out any 'direction' given otherwise, unless and until it is confirmed in writing.

(c) Under no circumstances should the Sub-Contractor follow the procedure provided by DOM/1 Clause 4.4 of NSC/C Clause 3.3.3, for him to confirm a Direction issued otherwise than in writing. This procedure is fraught with difficulty for Sub-Contractors; they are under no obligation to relieve Contractors of their duty to issue directions in writing, and they should not encourage sloppy practices by Contractors.

(d) Neither should the Sub-Contractor act on any 'instruction', whether given orally or in writing, which he receives from anyone other than the Contractor – e.g. Architect, Consultant, Clerks of Works, Building Inspector, etc. – until such an instruction has been confirmed as a written Direction by the Contractor.

(e) Architects in particular do not always fully appreciate the effects of their Instructions in terms of delay and/or cost. When the effects become apparent, they may well regret their action, especially if they had acted without authority from the Employer. To avoid the obvious problems which may well result, Sub-Contractors should, on receipt of a Contractor's Direction, give an estimate to the Contractor, in writing, of what the likely effects will be.

4. Late instructions

The programme agreed with the Contractor may have provided that some further information regarding the Sub-Contract Works would be provided at specific dates during the Sub-Contract period. In such cases the Sub-Contractor should not rely on that as satisfying the requirement to apply for instructions, drawings, details and levels. He should monitor the programme, and remind the Contractor of the requirement, in writing, a week or so in advance.

The Contractor may genuinely think that he has provided all that the Sub-Contractor will require, whereas the Sub-Contractor may think that further drawings or details will be forthcoming. Such an undesirable 'falling between stools' can be prevented if the Sub-Contractor considers well ahead and tells the Contractor in good time what further drawings or details he will require.

5. Management supervision

The Sub-Contractor's Contracts Manager should appreciate that on-site staff are subject to many pressures and can become over-whelmed by day-to-day problems to the detriment of forward planning. He should therefore, in addition to supervising off-site staff, also monitor on-site activities, consider future requirements, and give support to on-site staff. He should also check to see that all contract provisions are being complied with.

Friction can often arise between on-site staff and other persons connected with the Works, of whom there are many, including Architects, Consultants, Clerks of Works, Building Inspectors, other Sub-Contractors, Employer's representatives, etc. The Contracts Manager should monitor such situations and take such action as is necessary to prevent such friction getting out of hand.

Quality control is a most important function on all Sub-Contracts. Sub-Contractors are not entitled to have this service performed for them by others, to their quite justified annoyance, as is all too often the case. Sub-Contractors should appoint a member of their off-site staff to exercise quality control, and his task should be to check the work as it progresses, and to ensure that any deficiencies are corrected promptly and efficiently.

6. Meetings

Meetings can be dangerous, especially site meetings. Sub-Contractors should insist on a proper agenda being provided together, where appropriate, with reports on matters to be discussed, in order that the relevant matters may be considered in advance, and that appropriate staff may be delegated to attend.

If *ad hoc* meetings take place where no agenda is provided, the person attending should make it clear that any decisions which may be reached, and which affect the Sub-Contract, are conditional on their being confirmed from head office.

In all cases, the person attending a meeting must be instructed to take detailed notes of all matters which are discussed and, more importantly, of all decisions which are taken, and to submit these immediately to the Contracts Manager, in order that he may decide what action, if any, should be taken. In due course, these notes should be compared with the minutes when these are issued, and the Contracts Manager should immediately challenge any minute with which he has any disagreement.

7. Records

The value of maintaining thorough and comprehensive written records cannot possibly be overstated. Knowledge that such records exist can often deter a potential opponent from taking action. If, however, the Sub-Contractor does get involved in legal proceedings, such records will prove to be invaluable – see reference 24 to Chapter 3 – Contractors.

In addition to contractual records, dated notes of all telephone calls and other discussions should be kept, and all but trivial matters should be immediately confirmed in writing.

Where appropriate, a photographic record should be kept, to illustrate:

(a) The state of the Works and progress, which should be taken at no more than weekly intervals.
(b) Any constructional difficulties as may occur.
(c) Any work which has been condemned or criticised by the Architect, Consultants, Clerks of Works, Building Inspectors, etc.
(d) Any parts of the design of the Works which it is suspected are likely to prove defective, and about which the Contractor, and a Consultant where appropriate, has been warned.

The photographs should be taken with a camera which automatically records the date on the film. However, since it will be known that the dating mechanism can be altered, each batch of prints should also be signed and date-stamped by the processor.

G Completion

A frequent complaint against Sub-Contractors is a failure to bring the Works to a proper state of completion and/or being dilatory in effecting completion. This can have serious consequences for Sub-Contractors, since it can lead to:

1. Claims being made by the Contractor and/or the Employer against the defaulting Sub-Contractor.
2. The Sub-Contractor being put in a weaker position regarding any existing dispute(s).
3. Delayed payments.
4. The Contractor being highly unco-operative with a Domestic Sub-Contractor in agreeing the date of Practical Completion.
5. Late issue by the Architect of the Certificate of Practical Completion in relation to a Nominated Sub-Contractor's works.

For these reasons alone, it is most important that the Sub-Contract Works should be brought to a proper state of completion promptly and efficiently and, if any items affecting the Sub-Contract Works appear on a 'snagging list' issued by the Contractor, these should receive immediate and conscientious attention.

The ultimate responsibility for ensuring that this is done should rest with the member of the Sub-Contractor's staff charged with providing quality control services. His task should be to identify any incomplete or defective items, and to ensure that these are corrected promptly and efficiently. This is particularly important where the Sub-Contract involves mechanical or electrical services which must be tested prior to commissioning.

Release of the first moiety of retention is of importance to all Sub-Contractors, particularly when the Sub-Contract Works are carried out and completed in the early stages of the project as a whole – e.g. demolition, piling, other foundation works, etc. In this connection, the following contractual provisions should be noted.

1. Domestic Sub-Contractors

Domestic Sub-Contractors should notify the Contractor, as required by DOM/1 Clause 14.1, when in their opinion the Sub-Contract Works are completed, but it should be noted that DOM/1 Clause 14.2 gives the Contractor the right to dissent.

If the Contractor does not dissent, Practical Completion will be deemed to have occurred on the date of the Sub-Contractor's notification, and the first moiety of retention will be due for release.

If the Contractor does dissent, the Sub-Contractor should attempt to agree an alternative date for Practical Completion with the Contractor:

(a) If an alternative date is agreed, Practical Completion will be deemed to have occurred on the agreed date, and the first moiety of retention will be due for release.

(b) If an alternative date for Practical Completion cannot be agreed, the Sub-Contractor should, albeit grudgingly, accept the date put forward by the Contractor, because otherwise the first moiety of retention will not be due for release until the Architect issues the Certificate of Practical Completion under the Main Contract Clause 17.1, and that could result in a very long delay.

2. Nominated Sub-Contractors

Under NSC/C, the release of the first moiety of retention should present no problem even for those Sub-Contractors whose works are carried out and completed in the early stages of the project. The rules relating to releases of retention are those set out in Clause 30.4 of the Main Contract. Clause 30.4.1.3 provides that the first moiety of retention is due for release when the Architect issues the Certificate of Practical Completion in relation to the Sub-Contract Works (Clause 35.16 of the Main Contract).

Delays in the issue of Certificates of Practical Completion in relation to the Sub-Contract Works are not uncommon. So, when a Sub-Contractor is of the opinion that the Sub-Contract Works have reached the stage of Practical Completion, he should so notify the Contractor, who is then under a duty to immediately pass a copy of the notification to the Architect.

H Defects Liability Period

If earlier recommendations have been followed, the Sub-Contract accounts and applications will have been as up to date as is possible when Practical Completion occurs. Further applications for payment can, and should, be made after Practical Completion, as soon as these are justified by further valuations. If this recommendation is also followed, early agreement of final accounts will have been achieved and only retention will be left outstanding for final payment.

1. Domestic Sub-Contractors

This recommendation is of particular importance to Domestic Sub-Contractors because, by virtue of DOM/1 Clause 21.9, final payment is not due until seven days after the Architect has issued the Final Certificate under the Main Contract. That could result in a considerable delay, especially for Sub-Contractors whose works are carried out and completed in the early stages of the project.

As with all applications, full details must be supplied to substantiate the valuation in order to satisfy the requirements of DOM/1 Clause 21.1.4.

2. Nominated Sub-Contractors

The recommendation is also of importance to Nominated Sub-Contractors:

(a) As recommended earlier, notwithstanding that valuations of Sub-Contract Works are to be prepared by the Architect or Quantity Surveyor, Sub-Contractors should make applications as provided by NSC/C Clauses 4.15.1 and 4.15.2.
(b) By virtue of Clause 30.1.3 of the Main Contract, the Architect is under a duty to issue further Interim Certificates after Practical Completion, as and when further amounts are payable.
(c) The Sub-Contract expects the final accounts to be prepared as soon as possible after Practical Completion. Therefore, Sub-Contractors should be careful to comply with NSC/C Clause 4.23 or 4.24, whichever is applicable.

The recommendation is of particular importance to Nominated Sub-Contractors who have entered into Employer/Nominated Sub-Contractor Agreements NSC/W, especially when the Sub-Contract Works are carried out and completed in the early stages of the project.

By virtue of Clause 35.17 of the Main Contract, the Architect may issue an Interim Certificate to include final payment to a Sub-Contractor at any time after issuing the Certificate of Practical Completion in relation to the Sub-Contract Works as required by Clause 35.16 of the Main Contract. But, in any case, the Architect must issue this Interim Certificate not later than 12 months after issuing the relevant Certificate of Practical Completion.

If a Sub-Contractor is dissatisfied with the amount of the final payment, and he cannot get the amount adjusted, he should immediately invoke the provisions of NSC/C Clause 4.20. However, invoking these provisions is a highly technical matter, about which legal advice should always be sought.

During the Defects Liability Period, the Contractor is entitled to issue a Direction, whether or not as a result of an Architect's Instruction, calling on a Sub-Contractor to make good any defect in the Sub-Contract Works which may appear, and which requires immediate attention. These should be dealt with promptly in order to avoid, or reduce the possibility of, consequential damage.

J Feedback

1. All Sub-Contractors

At the end of the Defects Liability Period, the Architect has the power to issue a schedule of defects, and the Contractor will send Sub-Contractors such part(s) of the schedule as affects any of the Sub-Contract Works. The person delegated to provide quality control services should immediately inspect the items to see that all are valid and, if so, he should ensure that prompt attention is given to the necessary remedial work, so as to avoid causing delay in obtaining final payment.

Care should be taken when considering the items because it is not unknown for some items to be included which are not defects but which constitute variations. These should be challenged. Neither the Contractor nor the Architect is empowered to issue variation instructions after Practical Completion, so if the Sub-Contractor should be requested to carry out further work, he can either decline or set his own terms for doing so.

All the papers arising in the course of the project should be sorted, all duplicates and other non-essential papers should be discarded, and the remainder should be preserved for at least 10 years.

The Contracts Manager should carefully consider all that has occurred, from the original enquiry to the end of the contract, in order to see what lessons are to be learned from the experience gained.

2. Nominated Sub-Contractors

If early final payment has not been made, Clause 30.7 of the Main Contract will be important to a Sub-Contractor. This provides that not less than 28 days before the issue of the Final Certificate to the Contractor, the Architect must issue an Interim Certificate releasing final payments to all Nominated Sub-Contractors.

It is the Architect's duty, under Clause 35.13.1.2 of the Main Contract, to immediately notify Nominated Sub-Contractors of the amount of their final payments which have been included in the Interim Certificate.

The provisions relating to the issue of the Final Certificate are set out in Clause 30.8 of the Main Contract. The Architect has a duty under this clause to inform Nominated Sub-Contractors of the date of its issue. It is very important that Sub-Contractors should be aware that, by virtue of Clause 30.9 of the Main Contract, they would lose the right to challenge the amounts of their final payments 28 days after the issue of the Final Certificate.

Therefore, if a Nominated Sub-Contractor is dissatisfied with the amount of the final payment, and cannot get the amount adjusted, he should, well before the expiration of the 28 days, invoke the provisions of NSC/C Clause 4.20. However, as has been mentioned, invoking the provisions of NSC/C Clause 4.20 is a highly technical matter, about which legal advice should always be sought.

5

Building Owners and Project Managers

Attention has been drawn in the Introduction to the significance and importance of the 'Simon' Report, an extract of the crucial paragraphs of which is attached hereto as Appendix 1. The statement in that Report of greatest relevance to building owners is that set out in the final paragraph of Section 26:

> One of the major reforms in the building industry, therefore, is the education of the building owner to adopt businesslike methods in the preliminaries of the contract.[1]

In this chapter, the term "Building Owner" refers not only to private individuals but also to corporate bodies. Such bodies should always appoint one person with sole responsibility for all dealings with those to be engaged on the project. Such persons are generally referred to as "Project Managers".

For the sake of simplicity, from the point at which an architect is engaged, Building Owners and Project Managers will be referred to as "the Employer", which is the contractual term for building owners.

As explained in the Introduction, it is not only those directly involved in building projects who suffer damage when claims arise and become the subject of formal disputation. The enormous amount of non-productive expenditure is a massive drain on the national economy and it is Employers who could have the greatest effect of reducing this damage and, in the process, achieve great benefits for themselves.

Of those directly involved in building projects it is Employers who suffer most, and sadly this is often through no fault of their own. In the case of private individuals, the cause is an understandable ignorance of the complex processes involved in building contracting, and lack of good advice and/or service from their professional agents. In the case of corporate bodies, where it is shareholders, tax and charge payers who are the innocent sufferers, ignorance is no excuse, because those persons appointed as Project Managers should be properly qualified and fully aware of the causes of claims and how to avoid or reduce their incidence.

All Employers should appreciate the simple fact that 'claims'[2] only arise when changes occur after the terms of the building contract have been agreed and the Contract[3] has been executed. For commercial reasons, the Contract apportions the risks involved in changes as between the parties. Changes can be conveniently divided into four categories, all having differing effects for the Employer:

1. Changes in this category are listed as Relevant Events in Clauses 25.4.1, 2, 3, 4, 9, 10 and 11 of the Contract. Because such changes are not caused by anyone directly involved in the project, the risks are divided between the parties – the Employer bears the risk of delay, and the Contractor the risk of additional costs.

   Claims in this category are limited to the Contractor's entitlement to extensions of the Contract period. Disputes in this category can arise between the Architect and the Contractor as to whether or not an extension of time is justified and, if it is, as to its length.
2. Changes in this category are listed as a Relevant Event in Clause 25.4.7 of the Contract. These changes are brought about by acts or omissions of Nominated Sub-Contractors or Nominated Suppliers. Because such changes are not caused by either the Contractor, Architect or Employer, the risks are borne by the parties jointly. The Employer bears the risk of any resulting delay, and the Contractor bears the risk of any additional costs, as with category 1.

   However, there are two essential differences:

(a) The Employer will be able to recover any damages for non-completion on time, which he has lost as a result of delayed

completion, **provided** that he had entered into an Employer/
Nominated Sub-Contractor Agreement NSC/W with the
defaulter.

This is a complex procedure, and that is the most important
reason why the Employer should insist that there shall be no
Nominated Sub-Contractors or Suppliers, unless they are
truly unavoidable, and certainly none whose appointment is
delayed until after the Contractor has been appointed.

(b) The Contractor will be able to recover his additional costs
from the defaulter.

3. Changes in this category are listed as Relevant Events in Clauses
25.4.5 and 6 of the Contract. These changes are brought about by
acts or omissions of the Architect, and all risks are therefore
borne by the Employer. Claims will involve not only extensions
of the Contract period, but also the Contractor's entitlement to be
reimbursed, by the Employer, with the additional costs which
result from the delay to, and/or disruption of, his and his Sub-
Contractor's programmes.

Architects may not be personally responsible for these acts or
omissions, because they may be due to variations to the Works
requested by the Employer, or to unforeseen contingencies. For
instance, no matter how efficiently the pre-contract site investigation may have been carried out, bad ground may still be
discovered, resulting in changes to foundation requirements. A
further possibility is that whilst changes can only be ordered by
the Architect, it may be that others, such as Consultants, may be
responsible for the acts or omissions in question.

This is the most common cause of disputes between the
Architect and/or the Quantity Surveyor, and the Contractor as to
the latter's entitlements, especially when:

(a) Either the Architect or Quantity Surveyor, or both are over-
zealous in misguided attempts to protect their client, the
Employer – what are referred to in the industry as 'boss's
men'.

(b) The Architect is personally responsible for these acts or
omissions. It is sad to say that disputes can arise when he,
possibly aided and abetted by the Quantity Surveyor, denies
or reduces the Contractor's true entitlements due to being
anxious to avoid a possible negligence action being brought
against him by the Employer.

4. Changes in this category are listed as Relevant Events in Clauses 25.4.8, 12 and 13 of the Contract. As these changes are caused by acts or omissions by the Employer himself, for which he is entirely responsible, all risks are therefore borne by him. As with category 3, claims will involve not only extensions of the contract period, but also the Contractor's entitlement to be reimbursed, by the Employer, the extra cost resulting from the delay to, and/or disruption of, his programme.

Again, disputes do arise between the Architect and/or the Quantity Surveyor and the Contractor as to the latter's entitlements, especially when either or both are over-zealous in misguided attempts to protect the Employer.

The effect of claims by the Contractor which is common to all categories is that the Employer will get his building later than planned and in some cases this could have serious consequences, especially for commercial or Local Authority Employers. However, Employers should be advised that such delays may be reduced, if not avoided altogether, either by the omission of non-essential work, or by agreement with the Contractor for the remaining work to be accelerated, or by a combination of the two.

In addition, changes under all categories will cause extra cost to the Employer, and that extra cost could be very considerable with changes under categories 3 and 4 in particular. Furthermore, it is disputes under these categories which provide the most fertile ground for complex and expensive legal proceedings.

Whilst there is nothing that the Employer can do to avoid changes under categories 1 and 2, it must be patently obvious that, in his own interests, the Employer should do everything possible to avoid changes under categories 3 and 4.

The principal reasons why changes in categories 3 and 4 occur were set out in the 'Simon' Report:

(a) Insufficient pre-contract preparation of the particulars of the work to be carried out.
(b) Extensive variation orders after the contract is placed.[4]

As will be seen from Appendix 4 (Sections 25 and 26) reproduced here, the Report identified the cause as being due to building owners (Employers) seeking to insist on undue hurry. The blame for this, and the effect of such an approach, were clearly set out in the penultimate paragraph of Section 26:

> The responsibility for this rush and inefficiency lies squarely on the shoulders of the building owner. He can prevent it if he wishes. He thinks that he is going to get a cheaper and quicker job by rush methods, but he is profoundly mistaken. The work will take longer and cost more and he is the chief sufferer.[5]

It was, however, acknowledged that architects must bear some responsibility if they have not endeavoured to convince their building owner clients of the importance of having time to complete their designs in detail.

A similar message was conveyed in all subsequent government reports and publications and in documents published by, or on behalf of, the Royal Institute of British Architects (RIBA). For instance, in a leaflet published by the RIBA, and specifically addressed to building owners, it is said that:

> The all important date is not the day when work begins on site, but the day when the client occupies the building. Too early a start, before there has been enough time to complete the design, only leads to waste of time and money.[6]

The 'Simon' Report also clearly spelt out the first and most important step which a building owner should take when setting out on a building project:

> Much depends on the building owner. His business is to choose a good architect, to keep in touch with him, and to give him full opportunities of doing his work under the best conditions.[7]

Except for specialist work, or major projects, the building owner will always get the best service by engaging an architect based in the district in which the project is to be situated. For an inexperienced building owner, the choosing of an architect can be somewhat of a lottery, especially if a name is taken at random from the 'Yellow Pages'. The RIBA Directory of Practices, normally held in Reference Libraries, can be consulted, and this will give a better indication of the various practices related to areas, and details of the work in which each practice specialises and has experience.

However, it is far better to take the free advice offered by the local RIBA Clients' Advisory Service, details of which are given in the "Architects" section of the 'Yellow Pages'. A national Clients' Advisory Service is operated from the headquarters of the RIBA.[8]

Before the Architect is appointed, no matter how he was chosen, the Employer would be well advised to investigate his suitability for the commission, by asking for:

1. Details of similar projects to that envisaged for which the Architect was responsible. Most architects have brochures giving such details, but it is far better to go and see the actual projects.
2. References from other building owners of projects similar to that envisaged or, better still, if that is possible, to be introduced to them.

If as a result of these investigations the building owner is satisfied that the Architect in question is acceptable, he should make quite sure that a proper contract is entered into regarding the services which the Architect is to provide, and the charges which he will be entitled to make. Members of the RIBA are under a duty to ensure that these matters are settled before accepting a commission, and, in this connection, they will generally present prospective clients with one of two documents published by the RIBA as a basis for the contract.[9]

Building owners should know that architects are no longer in a position to dictate contractual terms to their clients, and that they are perfectly entitled to negotiate the terms of contracts with their clients. For example, the nature of the project may make it necessary for services to be provided by other persons, such as engineers and specialist contractors. Architects generally expect the building owner to engage, and accept responsibility for the work of, such other persons. However, for reasons which will be given later, a building owner, properly advised, will require the Architect himself to engage and be responsible for the work of such other persons.

Furthermore, because the terms offered by the RIBA documents referred to are extremely complex, the building owner should take advice from a solicitor experienced in such matters, prior to committing himself.

One further matter needs to be considered prior to the engagement of an architect, and this requires explanation. The process through which the normal building project passes is set out in a comprehensive document published by RIBA Publications Limited and entitled "The Plan of Work for design team operation". The various Work Stages are identified from A. 'Inception' to M. 'Feedback'. In relation to each Stage, the Plan of Work sets out its purpose and, in tabular form, the tasks to be performed, and the persons involved. An extract entitled "Outline Plan of Work" is reproduced here as Appendix 5.

A development of the Plan of Work entitled *Architect's Job Book*, also published by RIBA Publications Limited, sets out in detail all the work required to be carried out in relation to a building project. The *Client's Guide*, also published by RIBA Publications Limited, sets out, in relation to the Plan of Work Stages, the standard of service which the building owner can expect from the design team, and the input to be expected of the Employer.

The building owner should make it conditional to the Architect's engagement that he will:

1. Supply copies of the "Plan of Work", *Architect's Job Book* and *Client's Guide*.
2. Follow the provisions of the *Architect's Job Book* throughout the commission.
3. Provide a detailed report at the end of each Work Stage.
4. Not proceed with the next Work Stage until express authority to do so has been given.

From this point onwards, the building owner will be referred to as "the Employer", which is the term used in building contracts for building owners.

The following is a brief summary of the matters to be considered by the Employer, and the input required of him, in relation to each of the Work Stages:

A 'Inception'

The purpose of this Stage is to instruct the Architect, as first call adviser, as to the Employer's requirements in relation to a potential building project.

1. Sometimes it will be obvious that the Employer's requirements can only be satisfied by building work, either in the form of a new building on a particular site or by alterations, and perhaps extensions, to an existing building. Where that is not so, the Employer should set out his requirements in general terms so that the Architect, together with other advisors, can consider possible alternatives.
2. From this point on, the assumption will be made that the Employer's requirements can only be satisfied by building work.

In such cases, the Employer should set out his requirements in detail, from which the Architect will develop the 'brief'. In addition to setting out the functions which the project is to satisfy, the Employer should also provide details of ownership, required timescale, financial limits, etc.

3. The Employer should put the Architect in touch with such other persons – solicitors, accountants, land agents, etc. – who may be able to assist in providing relevant information. In particular, the Architect will need to consult the Employer's solicitors in order to discover what encumbrances (easements, covenants, planning refusals or conditional approvals, etc.), if any, apply to the site in question.

4. Because the brief is crucial to all subsequent Stages, the Employer should collaborate with the Architect in its production, and not give authority for the Architect to proceed to the next Stage until he is completely satisfied that the final version fully meets his requirements.

B 'Feasibility'

As the title suggests, the purpose of this Stage is for the Architect to consider all matters which may affect the fulfilment of the 'brief'.

1. In dealing with these studies, the Architect may well require expert assistance – civil, structural, mechanical and electrical engineers; landscape architects; interior designers, etc. Such experts are referred to as 'Consultants'. Under Clause 3.5 of the RIBA Architect's Appointment, the Architect may ask the Employer to agree to the appointment of Consultants and also to employ them. If the Employer agrees to employ Consultants, the group is then referred to as the 'design team'.

   However, the Employer, properly advised, would not agree to employ Consultants for three reasons:

   (a) As will be seen from Clause 3.6 of the RIBA Architect's Appointment, the Architect would have no responsibility for the competence of the Consultants or for the work entrusted to them.

      If a dispute were to arise between himself and a member(s) of the design team, the Employer could find himself faced with a variety of co-defendants instead of just one, the

Architect, and that would add enormously to his legal costs.

If the Employer were to require the Architect to employ, and be responsible for the work of, Consultants, as envisaged by Clause 2.45 of the RIBA Architect's Appointment, then, if a dispute were to arise, the Employer would only have one defendant – the Architect.

(b) If the Architect appoints, and becomes responsible for, the other members of the design team, he will then have a greater incentive to ensure that they are competent, that they perform their functions efficiently, and that there will be no 'falling between stools'.

(c) It is always best for the Architect to work with experts that he knows and can trust.

2. Because he will not be an expert on financial matters, the Architect will also ask the Employer to agree to the appointment of a quantity surveyor at this stage.

Those architects who have in-house quantity surveying departments may recommend that they be appointed, whilst those architects who do not have in-house quantity surveying departments may recommend a particular person or firm with whom they have worked in the past and have close ties.

The Employer should not agree to either of these recommendations because they can lead to 'cosy' relationships, and the Quantity Surveyor can tend to avoid 'biting the hand that feeds'. The value of the Quantity Surveyor to the Employer throughout a building project is so great that he should be totally independent of the design team. This was clearly expressed in a Policy Background Paper prepared by the Labour Party in the approach to the 1979 General Election:

> Perhaps most important, quantity surveying should evolve into a genuine cost control function. At present the quantity surveyor has very little to do with cost control – he acts essentially as a translator of design drawings into quantitative terms from which a contractor can, however inaccurately, calculate a tender price. Quantity surveyors could instead become technical auditors, employed by the client and independent of the design team. Appointments could be made from a register of approved quantity surveyors, and not on the basis of architects' recommendations.[10]

There are a number of quantity surveyors who offer this more general service, and the Employer should select and appoint one

of these, and make sure, in agreeing the terms of the appointment, that he will act entirely independently of the Architect.
This is the practice of many experienced building owners.

It is of course necessary for the Quantity Surveyor to co-
operate with the Architect at various stages, in order to monitor
the work of the design team; to provide cost advice; and to enable
him to provide financial reports to the Employer.

3. In due course the Architect and the Quantity Surveyor will
   provide reports on all aspects of feasibility, with recommendations as to future courses of action. These may be various:

   (a) That nothing has been discovered which casts doubt on the
       feasibility of the project, or requires the brief to be modified.
       In this case, the Employer should recheck the brief prior to
       authorising the Architect to proceed to the next Stage.
   (b) That the project could go ahead, but only if the brief were
       modified, for reasons indicated in the reports. In such a case,
       the Employer should consider the implications of the
       modifications, in conjunction with the Architect, Quantity
       Surveyor, and his other advisors, to see whether the project
       would be acceptable and viable in a modified form.
   (c) The reports may also give alternative solutions. For instance,
       a change of site or, if the problem is with the Planning
       Authority, that the Employer should consider his right of
       appeal.
   (d) That there are so many problems that the project should be
       aborted.

4. If the Employer's decision is that the project should go ahead in
   modified form, he should insist on the Architect providing a
   completely new brief, so that he, and everyone involved in the
   project, clearly understands what is then proposed, and what is
   expected of them.

C 'Outline Proposals'

As will be seen from the Outline Plan of Work (Appendix 5), prior
to its publication, this and the subsequent Stage (D. 'Scheme
Design'), were described as "Sketch Plans", which implied that the

first indication that the Employer had of the design team's interpretation of the brief was in a fully developed form.

Under such a regime, a considerable amount of abortive work, and lost time, resulted from any amendments to the proposals which the Employer might require. Sometimes, in order to avoid these problems, an Employer would approve the Sketch Plans even though they did not fully satisfy his requirements. Where this occurred, it often led to the Employer requiring alterations to be made at a later stage, when the effects of cost and time were infinitely greater, especially if it entailed the Architect having to issue variation orders. To avoid these problems, the Sketch Plans stage was divided into two Work Stages when the Plan of Work was published.

As the name suggests, the purpose of 'Outline Proposals' is for the design team to give the Employer, in as simplified form as is reasonable, their suggestions as to how the brief may be realised. The form which these may take will vary with the type of project. For instance, a full layout of accommodation may be provided for a private house, whereas line diagrams may be provided where the project is for an industrial complex. Indeed, with a complex project, the 'Outline Proposals' Stage may consist of a series of development studies.

The Quantity Surveyor's function at this stage is to monitor the design process and recommendations; to provide the Employer with approximate estimates of cost, and comparisons between these estimates and any financial limits which he may have set.

Because the design team has a great deal of work to do in the next Stage, in order to provide a fully developed design, the Employer should give the 'Outline Proposals' very careful consideration, and he should not hesitate to withhold his approval until he is completely satisfied.

When he has finally approved the 'Outline Proposals', the Employer should insist on the Architect providing an up-to-date version, in order that he, and everyone involved in the project, clearly understands what is then proposed and what is expected of them.

D 'Scheme Design'

This represents the final design stage in which input is required by the Employer. As indicated in the Outline Plan of Work (Appendix

5), the work to be carried out by the design team, in consultation with the Quantity Surveyor, is:

> To complete the brief and decide on particular proposals, including planning arrangement, appearance, structural method, outline specification, and cost, and to obtain all approvals.

The importance and significance of the Employer's approval of the 'Scheme Design' cannot be over-emphasised, as is explained in the *Client's Guide* (Appendix 6), and the Employer should take particular note of the following:

> It is clearly vital that before the client gives approval he is not merely satisfied with the scheme design but fully understands it.
>
> Although a request for an alternative scheme design is bound to cost time and money, the cost of any alteration to the scheme design at this stage will still be small compared with that of making changes later.[11]
>
> Approval of the final scheme design marks the watershed of the design phase. Every requirement should have been worked out within the cost plan and agreed by all concerned, and it is normally unwise and certainly expensive to alter the design after this. About half of the design team's work goes into the following stage – the translation of the scheme design into working drawings and specification notes which between them exactly describe every detail of the building's construction – and much of this work will have to be done again from the beginning if any change is made in the scheme design after it has been approved.[12]

An identical message is given in a government publication (Appendix 7) addressed to all building owners,[13] and in a leaflet published by the RIBA, and specifically addressed to building owners where it is said that:

> A change of mind by client or architect that can be effected with a rubber and pencil at this stage may be infinitely more difficult and costly twelve months later.[14]

The Employer should also note the warning given at the end of the 'Scheme Design' Stage in the Outline Plan of Work (Appendix 5):

> Brief should not be modified after this point.

The Employer should not hesitate to ask the Architect for further explanations if he does not fully understand the 'Scheme Design', and he should carefully check to see that it complies with all his requirements. Finally, the Employer should ask the Quantity Surveyor to provide an updated approximate estimate and a comparison between this and any financial limits which he may have set.

Only when he is completely satisfied should the Employer give authority for the Architect to proceed to the next Work Stage.

E 'Detail Design'

As will be seen from the Outline Plan of Work (Appendix 5), prior its publication this, and the subsequent Stages (F. 'Production Information', G. 'Bills of Quantities' and H. 'Tender Action'), were described as "Working Drawings". This arrangement was most unsatisfactory, since it failed to recognise that two quite distinct functions are involved – technical decision making and the production of the documents required by Contractors, Sub-Contractors and Suppliers. Where these functions were allowed to overlap, it was quite common for it to be necessary to carry out alterations to construction drawings and/or specifications as new decisions came to be made, leading to delay and abortive costs.

At the beginning of this Work Stage, the Quantity Surveyor should prepare a cost plan to enable each member of the design team to monitor design decisions. This ensures that any likely increase in cost over the Quantity Surveyor's approximate estimate is appreciated at an early stage, and appropriate action taken. If this practice is not followed, any increase in cost will not be discovered until the end of the Work Stage, when a considerable amount of redesign may be necessary, resulting in delay and abortive costs.

As the Outline Plan of Work (Appendix 5) stipulates, during the 'Detail Design' Stage, and prior to starting on the subsequent Stages, it is the design team's duty:

> To obtain final decisions on every matter related to design, specification, construction and cost.

The reason for sticking strictly to this regime is emphasised by the warning in the Outline Plan of Work (Appendix 5) which follows E. 'Detail Design':

> Any further change in location, size, shape, or cost after this time will result in abortive work.

Nevertheless, it is not uncommon for design team members to postpone decision making to a later date, all too often even after the Contractor has started work on site. This is achieved by the inclusion in the Bills of Quantities of provisional measurements;

Provisional or Prime Cost Sums; Nominated Sub-Contractors and Suppliers; or by producing outline rather than detailed drawings. This often occurs because a design team member has fallen behind the design period programme given to the Employer. The Employer should make sure that this does not happen, because it is the most common cause of claims.

Therefore, when authorising the Architect to proceed with the 'Detail Design Stage', he should make it abundantly clear, in writing, that he expects the relevant recommendations set in the 'Simon' Report to be followed:

> The owner should insist on the completion of detailed drawings and specifications by the architect and should himself do his thinking and make his final decisions on a careful study of these documents; he should not wait to see what the job looks like as it goes up and then change his mind or make new suggestions. The contract drawings and the bills of quantities should accurately represent the work which will ultimately be carried out.[15]
>
> In general, we recommend the existing practice under which the building owner places the whole of the work under one contract in the hands of a single general contractor and all specialists are his sub-contractors. Under this system the general contractor has, apart from his work as a builder, the responsibility for directing and co-ordinating the work of all sub-contractors, who may together carry out a considerable proportion of the value of the whole contract. It is of the first importance that the general contractor should, subject to the directions of the architect, be in full control of the whole of the executive work on site. It is, therefore, desirable that as much of the work as possible should be fully described in the bills of quantities for the main contract, and should be priced and carried out by the general contractor or by firms selected by him, with whom he is accustomed to work and in whom he has confidence. This should ensure the best conditions for the success of his management of the whole contract.[16]

Prior to authorising the Architect to proceed with the subsequent Stages, the Employer should require him to provide a report, and an undertaking, signed by all members of the design team, that all design decisions have been taken, that nothing is left to be decided at a later date, and that there will be no unauthorised Nominated Sub-Contractors or Suppliers.

It all too often happens that, as the work goes on, the Employer comes to realise that the standards of materials and workmanship are not as high as he had expected them to be. If the Architect confirms that the standards comply with the specification, most unfortunate situations are bound to arise:

1. The Employer will either have to:

   (a) Accept the lower standards, or
   (b) Authorise the Architect to correct the 'misunderstanding(s)' by issuing variation instructions to the Contractor.

2. Acceptance of the latter option will inevitably cause delay and extra cost, and probably disputes:

   (a) It will lead to the Contractor, and possibly Sub-Contractors, making claims not only for the additional cost, but also for extensions of time and disruption loss and/or expense.
   (b) There is likely to be a dispute between the Employer, Architect, Quantity Surveyor and possibly Consultants, as to who was responsible for the 'misunderstanding(s)', especially if any of the professionals seek to make extra charges.[17]

It is therefore essential that the Employer should, at this Stage, consult with the Architect to ensure that the standards which are to be specified in the next Work Stage will be as he requires them to be.

F 'Production Information'

No input by the Employer will be required in this Stage.

During this Work Stage, the design team will convert the approved 'Detail Design' into production drawings, details, specifications, etc., and these will then be passed to the Quantity Surveyor.

G 'Bills of Quantities'

Prior to authorising the Quantity Surveyor to proceed with the preparation of the Bills of Quantities, the Employer should require him to confirm that:

1. Subject to minor queries, full details have been provided in the documents sent to him by the Architect.
2. There will be no need for provisional measurements, Provisional or Prime Cost Sums, or provisions for unauthorised Nominated

Sub-Contractors or Suppliers to be included in the Bills of Quantities.

If the Quantity Surveyor cannot give these confirmations, the Employer should call a meeting with the Architect and the Quantity Surveyor to discuss the matter, and he should not authorise the Quantity Surveyor to proceed until he is quite satisfied that these are wholly unavoidable.

H 'Tender Action'

At this Stage, the Employer will be asked to assist in the completion of the tender documents. In particular, he will be asked to:

1. Approve the tendering procedure to be adopted, and to approve the suggested list of tenderers prepared by the Architect and/or Quantity Surveyor. Unless there are compelling reasons, the Employer should not object to any of the nominees, nor should he insist on the inclusion of contractors against whom the Architect or Quantity Surveyor expresses reasonable objection.
2. Agree on the contract start date, i.e. the date on which possession of the site can be given to the successful contractor. The Employer should be very careful in regard to this matter because serious consequences would follow if possession was not given on the agreed date.
3. Set the amount of Damages for non-completion (Clause 24.2.1 of the Contract). On this matter, the Employer should not only consider suggestions made by the Architect and Quantity Surveyor, but should also take advice from his accountants and solicitors because he could suffer if the rate is set either too high or too low.
4. Stipulate if the period for:
   (a) The issue of Interim Certificates (Clause 30.1.3 of the Contract) is to be other than monthly.
   (b) Honouring amounts included in Interim and Final Certificates (Clauses 30.1.3 and 30.8.2 of the Contract) is to be other than 14 days.
5. Give details of the addressee if the Employer requires that tenders are to be delivered to someone other than the Architect or Quantity Surveyor.

The Employer should require:

1. The Quantity Surveyor to give an undertaking that all matters have been covered by the Bills of Quantities, and that there are no unauthorised provisional measurements, or Provisional or Prime Cost Sums.
2. The Architect to confirm that all drawings, details and other technical information are complete, accord with those on which the Bills of Quantities are based, and that they will either be provided to, or made available for inspection by, all tenderers.
3. The Architect to confirm that the tendering procedure being adopted is in accordance with the NJCC Code of Procedure.[18]

At the end of this Stage, the Architect and/or the Quantity Surveyor will provide the Employer with a report on the result of tendering, and will make recommendations as to the tender which they consider most suitable for acceptance. In order to comply with the rules of the NJCC Code, there would have to be compelling reasons if the recommendation was for the acceptance of any tender other than the lowest. The Employer should carefully consider the recommendations and give instructions as appropriate.

Up to this point, the Architect's and the Quantity Surveyor's sole responsibilities are to the Employer, their client. However, the Employer should appreciate that if the Architect and the Quantity Surveyor are appointed under Articles 3A (or 3B if appropriate) and 4 of the Contract, that is no longer the case once the Contract is let. From that point on, whilst they still owe continuing duties to the Employer, they will both have legal and professional duties to act independently and impartially as between the Employer and the Contractor. If the Employer does not understand this changed situation, he should call on the Architect and Quantity Surveyor to explain it to him.

J 'Project Planning'

Acceptance of the relevant tender effectively creates a contract between the Employer and the Contractor. Prior to this, therefore, the Employer should:

1. Check to ensure that possession of the site can be given to the Contractor on or before the date given in the tender documents.

2. Do a final check to ensure that no circumstances have arisen which make changes in the work to be carried out, or contract provisions, necessary or desirable. The Employer should appreciate that changes of any kind after this point will invariably cause delay and additional cost:

> It cannot be too strongly emphasised that the cost and delay which the client will have to bear if he insists on a departure from the brief after building has started may well be out of all proportion to the advantages he may gain, unless some major change has occurred in his circumstances and requirements since the sketch design was approved. The work on the site is the outcome of months of planning, scheduling, ordering and instruction. Any alteration, however slight in itself, makes it necessary to stop, change and remotivate a very complicated and cumbersome mechanism. It undermines morale on the site and weakens the sense of urgency and responsibility in all concerned. Much of the inefficiency of which the building industry is accused might be laid more properly at the door of diligent clients who are anxious to have a first-class job but fail to realise what havoc their second thoughts can cause – *see Appendix 7, Section 30.*

3. Make arrangements to ensure that payments in respect of Interim Certificates will be made within the period of honouring – Clause 30.1.3 of the Contract.
4. Remind the Architect, in writing, that:

   (a) He is to provide monthly reports covering all matters affecting the Works, including a financial statement prepared in conjunction with the Quantity Surveyor and other consultants where appointed.[19]
   (b) Under no circumstances whatsoever is he to issue any variation instruction under Clause 13.2 of the Contract without the Employer's express authority.[20] If the Architect is authorised to issue a variation instruction, it must be in writing, with a copy being sent to the Employer.
   (c) He must inform the Employer at once "if the total authorised expenditure or the building contract period is likely to be materially varied".[21]

   If either of the situations referred to in (b) and (c) should occur, the Employer should call on the Architect and Quantity Surveyor to consider and advise as to what avoidance action(s) might be possible.
5. Insist on the contract documents being executed prior to work commencing on site.

6. Where appropriate, appoint a person to liaise with the Architect, and Clerk of Works where one is appointed, during the carrying out of work on site. This person should be given strict instructions that:

   (a) No approval is to be given for the Architect to issue any variation instruction without having first explained the reason for, and obtained express permission from, the Employer.
   (b) No visits are to be made to the site unless accompanied by the Architect (or Clerk of Works), unless authorised in advance by the Employer.
   (c) Any comments as to the Works are to be made only to the Architect (or Clerk of Works), and never in the presence of the Contractor, his operatives or representatives, or any Sub-Contractors or their operatives or representatives.
   (d) Regular reports should be made to the Employer, especially as to progress, the quality of the Works, and any indications of friction between the contractual officials and the Contractor or Sub-Contractors.

The Employer should appreciate that the vast majority of claims result from disputes between the Contractor and the Architect and/or the Quantity Surveyor. All too often, the first indication that the Employer has of such disputes is when the Contractor threatens, or invokes, the arbitration provisions, by which time matters may have gone beyond the point where formal proceedings can be avoided or disputes compromised.

Contractors think that they should only deal with the Architect and/or the Quantity Surveyor, and do not appreciate that this is not a rule, but only a convention. Contractors should know that the Architect and the Quantity Surveyor are not parties to the Contract, but only officials appointed under it. The parties to the Contract are the Employer and the Contractor, and it is their interests which are at stake when disputes arise and cannot be resolved.

For this reason, the Employer should, at the very commencement of the Contract:

1. Establish direct lines of communication and good relations with the Contractor, and make it quite clear that if claims arise which they cannot resolve with the contractual officials, the Contractor should not hesitate to get in touch with him.

2. Instruct the contractual officials that he is to be immediately notified:

    (a) Of any claim made by the Contractor, with an explanation as to the reason(s) for the claim, the manner in which they propose to deal with it, and the effect, if any, which this will have on the progress and/or cost of the Works.

    (b) If the Contractor is dissatisfied with the manner in which the claim has been dealt with by the contractual officials, and a dispute has arisen, or is likely to arise.

If the Employer is sensible, he will be only too pleased that he has been given the opportunity to intervene before matters get out of hand and his interests are irreparably compromised. He should call a meeting with the Contractor and the Architect and/or the Quantity Surveyor, so that he can hear what the dispute is all about, and in the hope that a solution may be found.

At such a meeting the Employer should bear in mind that the reason why the Contractor is unable to obtain satisfaction of the claim from the contractual officials may be because one (or other or both) of them:

    (a) Is being over-zealous in a misguided attempt to protect the Employer – through being what the industry refers to as 'boss's men' – or,

    (b) Realising that he is responsible for the claim being made, is trying to protect himself against a possible negligence claim by the Employer.

Bearing this in mind, if the matter cannot be resolved at the meeting, the Employer should ask the Contractor to agree, on a 'without prejudice' basis, to a contractual expert being asked to review the matter and give an opinion. Great care should be taken in appointing such an expert* because the last thing that is wanted is a person, and there are some, who will say only what they think the Employer wants to hear. When such an expert is appointed, it should be made clear that what is required is a strictly professional and independent opinion.

The Employer may care to know that it used to be a tradition that as soon as a building was wind and weather proof, the workmen

---

* An experienced arbitrator would be ideal.

would attach a flag to the highest part of the building. This was a signal that if the Employer was satisfied with the work and progress thus far, he would bring appropriate liquid refreshments to the site for consumption by the workmen at what was called a 'topping-out ceremony'. Revival of this ceremony would do a great deal in terms of improving relations, and it would lead to the Employer getting even better service on the remaining, critical, stages of the work!

L 'Completion'

Towards the end of the Contract, the Employer should:

1. Ask the Architect for early provision of:
   (a) 'As-built' drawings.[22]
   (b) Guidance on maintenance,[23] which should be in the form of a maintenance handbook.
2. Ensure that his operating and maintenance staff are appointed in good time, and that they are provided with a copy of the maintenance handbook.
3. Ensure that those to be responsible for mechanical and electrical installations are made fully acquainted with the systems, that they are present when the final tests are carried out, and that they are also provided with a copy of the maintenance handbook.
4. Make diary reminders regarding items which require regular or periodic maintenance.
5. Make arrangements for his own insurances to take over when the Contractor's insurances lapse – which will occur when the Architect issues the Certificate of Practical Completion.

The Employer should be aware that teething troubles are not unlikely with all new buildings, and that mechanical systems need fine tuning, particularly in the early stages of use. He should not therefore be unduly surprised if defects do occur. If any which require urgent attention do occur, he should notify the Architect who will make appropriate arrangements for their rectification.

It would not be in the Employer's interests to call for non-urgent defects to be rectified immediately. It is much better to wait for these to be attended to at the end of the Defects Liability Period. The Employer should make arrangements for the building and all its services to be monitored, and for a note to be kept of all defects, however minor. These should be listed, and a copy of the list should be passed to the Architect immediately prior to the expiration of the Defects Liability Period, who will then consider these when making his own final inspection, and arrange for the appropriate rectification works to be carried out.

After all defects have been rectified, the Architect will issue the Certificate of Making Good Defects, and this will bring the contract to a conclusion. All that will then remain will be for the Employer to honour the Final Certificate. However, the Employer should continue to monitor the building, and notify the Architect of any further defects which may manifest themselves.

References

1 "The Placing and Management of Building Contracts", Report of the Central Council for Works and Buildings, London: HMSO, 1944, Section 26, final paragraph, page 11.
2 See Preface for definition of the types of 'claims' with which this book is primarily concerned.
3 See Preface for type of contract with which this book is primarily concerned.
4 "The Placing and Management of Building Contracts", Report of the Central Council for Works and Buildings, London: HMSO, 1944, Section 24, page 10.
5 ibid, Section 26, penultimate paragraph, page 11.
6 *Working With Your Architect*, London: RIBA Publications Limited, 1964, page 13.
7 "The Placing and Management of Building Contracts", Report of the Central Council for Works and Buildings, London: HMSO, 1944, Section 25, first paragraph, page 10.
8 Royal Institute of British Architects, 66 Portland Place, London W1N 4AD. Telephone: 071–580 5533.
9 "Architect's Appointment"; "Standard Form of Agreement for the Appointment of an Architect (SFA/92)", Royal Institute of British Architects.
10 "Building Britain's Future – Labour's policy on construction, A Policy Background Paper", October 1977, The Labour Party, Transport House, Smith Square, London.
11 *Client's Guide*, London: RIBA Publications Limited, 1973, Section 4, page 17, first paragraph.
12 ibid, third paragraph.

13 R & D Building Management Handbook *Preparing to Build*, London: HMSO, 1965, pages 20/21, paragraphs 21 and 22.
14 *Working With Your Architect*, London: RIBA Publications Limited, 1964, pages 13/14.
15 "The Placing and Management of Building Contracts", Report of the Central Council for Works and Buildings, London: HMSO, 1944, Section 26, second paragraph, page 11.
16 ibid, extracts from Sections 46 and 47, pages 18/19.
17 For example, "Architect's Appointment", Royal Institute of British Architects, Clause 4.37.b.
18 Code of Procedure for Single Stage Selective Tendering 1989, National Joint Consultative Committee for Building, London: RIBA Publications Limited.
19 "Architect's Appointment", Royal Institute of British Architects, Clause 1.23.
20 ibid, Clause 3.3.
21 ibid, Clause 3.4.
22 ibid, Clause 1.25.
23 ibid, Clause 1.26.

6
Advisors to potential disputants

As has been explained in earlier chapters, the parties to the Contract, and therefore the parties to potential disputes, are the Contractor and the Employer. Yet the most common cause of disputes results from the acts and/or omissions of others – the Architect, Quantity Surveyor and Consultants – none of whom are parties to the Contract and therefore not liable to any legal sanction under the Contract.

When claims arise which cannot be resolved by the contractual officers, the parties should appreciate that the only formal option is then to go to law. However, they ought also to appreciate that going to law, whether by arbitration or litigation, is a lengthy, harrowing and expensive procedure, at the end of which nobody wins except arbitrators, lawyers and expert witnesses. That being so, both parties would be well advised to be sensible, and seek other ways of settling their differences.

It is for this reason that it is recommended, in Chapters 3 and 5, that, at the very commencement of the Contract, the parties should establish direct lines of communication and good relations with each other in the hope that mutual respect and understanding will develop and, if things do go wrong, they will remain on speaking terms, and be co-operative in seeking a resolution of potential disputes short of taking formal proceedings.

For the same reason it is recommended, in Chapter 5, that the Employer should make it clear to the Contractor that he should not hesitate to get in touch with him if claims arise which cannot be resolved with the contractual officials, in order to give him the opportunity to intervene before matters get out of hand and his interests are irreparably compromised.

Contrary to rumour, and some unfortunate propaganda, it is the author's experience that Contractors are not 'money-grubbers', dedicated to extracting every last penny from a hapless Employer, or insisting on all provisions of the Contract in their favour being strictly adhered to. Contractors are generally quite prepared to compromise their claims, provided that the final outcome gives them a reasonable return. Particularly is this so when the Architect and Employer have been careful in the selection of tenderers.

Provided that the Employer is also reasonable, negotiation is therefore the first option open to the parties in avoiding formal proceedings. If either or both parties are not prepared to consider direct negotiations, and have instructed solicitors, it is to be hoped that the solicitors would suggest, as do the best practitioners, that they be given authority to investigate the possibility of arriving at a negotiated settlement.

If negotiations do not take place, or do take place but fail to result in a settlement, it is to be hoped that the parties will then consider other options or, if the parties have instructed solicitors, that the solicitors will encourage them to do so.

The most commonly occurring disputes as to claims can be roughly divided into three types, operating either individually or in combination:

1. Whether or not the Architect has correctly performed his duties, and exercised the discretion vested in him, under Clause 25.3 of the Contract regarding extensions of time, and/or under Clauses 26.1 and 34.3 of the Contract regarding loss and/or expense allegedly incurred by the Contractor.
2. Whether or not the Quantity Surveyor has correctly performed his duties, where instructed by the Architect under Clauses 26.1 and 34.3 of the Contract regarding the valuation of loss and/or expense incurred by the Contractor.
3. Whether or not the Quantity Surveyor has correctly performed his duties, and exercised such discretion as is vested in him, regarding valuations under Clauses 13.4, 30 and 37 of the Contract.

It will be obvious that, whilst matters of a strictly legal nature may be involved, the principal considerations are as to the facts, and the reaction of the contractual officials to those facts. If formal proceedings were to be instituted, the crucial contribution which would be made would be by experts, i.e. other building profession-als. If the proceedings were to be by way of arbitration, the arbitrator would be an expert. Therefore, if the parties have been unable or unwilling to negotiate a settlement, but are still anxious to avoid formal proceedings, they should consider the following further options:

1. To jointly appoint an expert* to consider the matter and provide a considered opinion. This may show that the differences between the parties are so small that they ought to be able to negotiate a settlement.

   If in the course of his considerations the expert should find a matter of strict law, he would probably be able to express an opinion on it. If either of the parties is not satisfied with what is strictly speaking an 'amateur' opinion, they can agree to ask the expert to take the opinion of Counsel which, under recent changes introduced by the Bar Council, they are now able to do without having to engage a solicitor.

2. To take advantage of the recently developed system known as "Alternative Dispute Resolution (ADR)" or "Mediation". This system, which is similar to ACAS in industrial disputes, is described as follows:

   > Where two people or companies are unable to resolve a particular problem they invite a neutral person to help them arrive at a solution. The neutral person, or Mediator, will work hard with each side and help them to understand better their own and the other person's position, and explore alternative solutions. By doing so the parties improve their chances of working out a solution to their mutual satisfaction.[2]

3. If the parties are not prepared to accept either of these options, they should each appoint an expert to consider the matter and provide a considered opinion. In making these appointments, the parties should know that, in any formal proceedings, the arbitrator (or judge) would issue directions that the parties' experts are to meet and agree, as far as possible, so as to limit the

---

* The type of expert will depend on the particular dispute. However, in the majority of cases, an experienced arbitrator would be an ideal choice.[1]

area of dispute, and then to issue a joint report setting out the residual areas of disagreement.

This is a very sensible course, and the parties should follow it by issuing similar instructions to their experts. The joint report setting out the residual areas of disagreement may well show that the differences between the parties are so small that they ought to be able to reach a settlement.

In the course of legal proceedings, in a process known as Discovery and Inspection, each party is obliged to list all documents touching the matters in dispute that are, or have been, "in their power or possession", and to make these available for inspection by the other party:

1. For the Contractor, the listing of documents is quite straightforward but, bearing in mind the amount of paper generated in building contracts, it is a mountainous task and therefore very time-consuming and extremely expensive.
2. For the Employer, the listing of documents is not so straightforward because of the phrase "in their power". Contrary to what they may believe, most of the papers held by those engaged by the Employer, including the Architect, Quantity Surveyor, Consultants, etc., are not in fact theirs – they belong to the Employer. They are therefore in his power, and he can demand that they be delivered to him provided that their charges have been paid. If he is not prepared to pay the charges, because he is in dispute as to the amount, he can still obtain possession of the papers by paying the disputed amount into court.

   The Employer's list must therefore include all the documents held by the Architect, Quantity Surveyor, Consultants, etc., in addition to his own, and this makes the listing equally time-consuming and expensive.

Whichever of the suggested options the parties choose, the cost of listing can be saved by the expert(s) being given unrestricted authority to examine all the papers relating to the Contract held on both sides, particularly those relating to the dispute in question.

If none of the suggested options is chosen, arbitration or litigation becomes inevitable. In these circumstances, the first thing that the parties' legal representatives should do would be to obtain reports from experts.

Unless the parties agree otherwise, Discovery and Inspection will not take place until very late in the proceedings, and these reports will be hampered by being based only on the documents held by the party by whom they are engaged. This can have two effects with related unfortunate and expensive results:

1. After the experts have eventually been able to inspect the documents held by the other party, their reports, and the Pleadings based upon them, may well have to be amended.
2. The meeting of experts will not take place until even later in the proceedings, i.e. after they have been able to inspect the documents held by the other party, and have amended their reports. It could well be that the experts may then find themselves much closer than they had originally believed to be the case.

It may well be the case that if the parties had received the more thorough experts' reports, and the joint report setting out the residual areas of disagreement, at an earlier stage, the possibility of a settlement being arrived at would be greatly increased, and an enormous amount of time and money saved as a result.

Parties getting involved in legal proceedings should therefore agree to appoint experts at an early stage, give them unrestricted authority to examine all the papers relating to the Contract held on both sides, and then to meet in order to provide a joint report setting out the residual areas of disagreement.

Clearly, the role of the expert is crucial in relation to all disputes which arise in building contracts. It goes without saying that experts should be well qualified and experienced in the subject matter. However, what is equally, if not more, important, is that those appointing them should ensure that they understand the true nature of their role, namely that if they are called to give evidence in any proceedings, whether by arbitration or litigation, they would be "assistants to the tribunal" or "witnesses for the court".

The reason for this is that judges are lay to technical matters, and even arbitrators cannot be expert in all the technical areas which may be involved in a building dispute. They therefore have no alternative but to decide technical issues on the basis of the evidence given by experts. Furthermore, expert evidence has to be given under oath, and that evidence is required to be the whole truth and nothing but the truth, not only in a factual sense, but also in a strictly professional sense.

The true expert will be able to say, and be proud to say, with hand on heart, that the evidence which he will give would be the same no matter by which of the parties he was engaged.

The importance of this matter was emphasised in the Foreword to a book addressed to potential expert witnesses:

> I do so for the purpose of stressing once again how much in a wide variety of cases the judiciary rely upon the candour and expertise of expert witnesses to enable justice to be done. In the very first chapter of this book, attention is drawn to the function of the expert witness as being to assist the tribunal to come to a true and proper decision. Honesty in expression of his opinion on matters within his field of expertise is a characteristic of experts with professional qualifications that I have always, and happily with justification, been able to take for granted.[3]

Unfortunately, not all judges have had the happy experience of expert witnesses as Lord Diplock appears to have had. Some persons called as experts have behaved so badly as to incur severe criticism by the judiciary. For instance, a judge once defined an expert as "a person who will come into court and completely contradict the evidence given by a similar expert called by the other party", and, in a recent building case,[4] the learned judge had this to say:

> It appeared to me that some (but by no means all) of the experts in this case tended to enter into the arena in order to advocate their client's case. This led to quite proper cross-examination on the basis: "You have assembled evidence and advanced explanations which you consider most likely to assist your client's case." It is much to be regretted that this had to be so. In their closing speeches counsel felt it necessary to challenge not only the reliability but also the credibility of experts with unadorned attacks on their veracity. This simply should not happen where the court is called upon to decide complex scientific or technical issues.
>
> It is in my view salutory to recall the observations of Lord Wilberforce in *Whitehouse v Jordan* [1981] 1 WLR 246 at page 256. "It is necessary that expert evidence presented to the court should be, and should be seen to be, the independent product of the expert, uninfluenced as to form or content by the exigencies of litigation. To the extent that it is not, the evidence is likely to be not only incorrect but self-defeating."

In appointing experts, the parties, or their solicitors, should therefore be careful to appoint only those persons who understand this position, and will faithfully follow what is to be expected of them. If they do, the residual differences between opposing experts will be, and indeed ought to be, so small that the possibility of a negotiated settlement is very greatly increased, and they will have done a great service for their respective clients and for society as a whole.

The last thing that is wanted are persons who will say only what they think will favour the case of the party by whom they are engaged. All too often, the author has found himself on opposite sides to such so-called 'experts'. In all cases their evidence was "not only incorrect but self-defeating", and it cost their clients very dear indeed.

In summary, if claims cannot be settled by the contractual officers, and the parties are unable to negotiate a settlement direct, those appointed to advise in respect of a building dispute should do everything possible to devise ways of avoiding the dispute resulting in legal proceedings, some of which have been suggested above.

Finally, even if the parties are not prepared to co-operate with each other, or are even 'at each other's throats', there is no excuse whatsoever for their experts to take sides and behave in a similar manner. To do so would put the so-called professional beyond contempt, and bring his professional body into disrepute.

References

1 Names of suitable persons may be obtained from the appropriate professional body (RIBA, RICS, CInst Arb., etc.), or from The British Academy of Experts, 90 Bedford Court Mansions, Bedford Avenue, London WC1B 4AE.
2 "What is Mediation?", ADR 1, The British Academy of Experts, April 1991. See also: "Mediation – Getting Started", ADR 2; and "Guidelines for Mediation", ADR 3, The British Academy of Experts, April 1991.
3 Foreword by Lord Diplock to *The Expert Witness*, 1982, R.H. Mildred FRICS FCIArb FFB, Past Chairman of the Chartered Institute of Arbitrators, George Godwin.
4 Per Garland J in *The University of Warwick* v *Sir Robert McAlpine and Others* [1988] 42 BLR 6, at pages 22/23.

Appendix 1

Relationships in conventional construction contracts

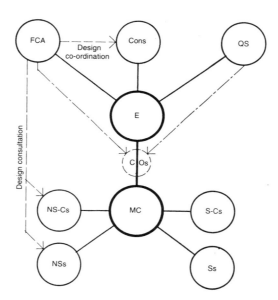

KEY

Cons : Consultants = Engineers: Structural, Mechanical, Electrical, Drainage, etc.; Interior Designers; Landscape Architects; other specialist designers and advisers.

COs : Contractual Officers = Persons appointed to carry out specified administrative functions under contract.

E : Employer = Client; Building Owner; etc.

FCA : First-call Advisor = Architect; Engineer; Landscape Architect; other, depending on type of contract.

MC : Main Contractor = Builder, Civil Engineering Contractor; Landscape Contractor; other, depending on type of contract.

NSs : Nominated Suppliers
Ns-Cs : Nominated Sub-Contractors } Appointed by MC to order of FCA.

QS : Quantity Surveyor

DSs : Domestic Suppliers
Ds-Cs : Domestic Sub-Contractors } Appointed by MC with permission of FCA.

Appendix 2

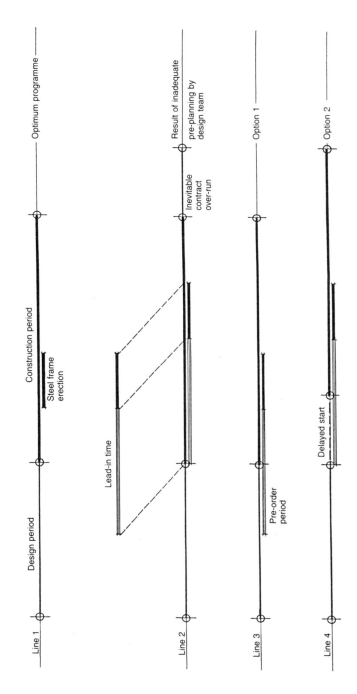

Line 1 —⊕———— Design period ———————⊕—— Construction period ——⊕—— Optimum programme ——

Steel frame erection

Line 2 —⊕———————— Lead-in time ———————⊕——— Inevitable contract over-run ——⊕—— Result of inadequate pre-planning by design team ——

Line 3 —⊕———————— Pre-order period ——⊕——————————⊕———————⊕—— Option 1 ——

Line 4 —⊕——— Delayed start ——⊕——————————⊕———————⊕—— Option 2 ——

Diagram showing need for pre-planning by design team and options for mitigation of delay costs.

Appendix 3

Simplified example of the financial implications for the building owner of inadequate pre-planning by design team

1. A small provincial office block of 3,000 sq.m. is to be demolished and the site redeveloped with a new office block of the same floor area.

2. Delay in achieving the contract Completion Date will cause prolongation costs for the building owner:

   (a) Loss of rents.
   (b) Contractor's loss and/or expense.

3. The optimum programme, including the design and contract periods, and the period for steel frame erection, are shown on Line 1 in Appendix 2.

4. Existing rents:

   (a) £140.00 sq.m. per annum.
   (b) £2.69 sq.m. per week.
   (c) Overall rents: 3,000 × £2.69   £8,070.00 per week.

5. New rents:

    (a) £2,260.00 sq.m. per annum.
    (b) £4.35 sq.m. per week.
    (c) Overall rents: 3,000 × £4.35   £13,050.00 per week.

6. Contractor's loss and or expense   £8,200 per week.

7. Prolongation costs to be borne by the
building owner resulting from the
'inevitable contract over-run' shown on
Line 2 in Appendix 2, assumed to be
10 weeks, will amount to:

    (£13,050.00 + £8,200.00 × 12   £255,000.00.*

8. Cost of Option 1 (pre-ordering preparatory
work by steelwork sub-contractor) shown on
Line 3 in Appendix 2   Nil.

9. Cost of Option 2 (postponing contract
start date) shown on Line 4 in Appendix 2   £49,800.00**

*This figure is based entirely on loss of rents and contractor's loss and/or expense, and takes no account of financing charges or other costs and expenses incurred by the building owner, which would include additional fees and expenses charged by members of the design team!
** This figure is the difference between existing and new rents, assuming that use of the existing building would continue during the postponement.

Appendix 4

Extract from Chapter 1 of the 'Simon' report

Pre-contract preparation – the time and progress schedule

22. Good practice in placing a contract for a large building has been as follows:

(a) The architect with the building owner has prepared a statement of the latter's requirements.

(b) He has selected the consultants and the quantity surveyor obtaining, where necessary, the approval of the building owner.

(c) He has prepared sketch plans and with the quantity surveyor a preliminary approximate cost.

(d) He has selected such sub-contractors as he has considered it necessary to nominate in advance of the signing of the contract.

(e) With the help of the consultants and the nominated sub-contractors he has prepared a full set of drawings and specifications.

(f) The quantity surveyor has prepared detailed bills of quantity, describing in words every service to be performed.

(g) Tenders have been obtained on the basis of the bills of quantities from a selected list of firms.

(h) The architect has with the building owner selected the general contractor.*

(i) He has with the consultants and quantity surveyor prepared the contract documents.

(j) The general contractor has signed the main contract and contracts with the sub-contractors – some nominated by the architect, some selected by himself.

23. On a very small job the procedure is of course much simpler; the local builder will usually quote a lump sum price, with perhaps a sketch showing what he intends to do, and will carry out the whole job himself. On a rather larger contract, the architect will generally make all the plans himself, and settle the contract with the builder on the basis of these plans. As the job gets bigger, the procedure approaches the more elaborate system described above.

24. This system has been gradually built up as the result of long experience. We regard it as being in general the right system, subject to certain conditions and modifications which we discuss in this and the following chapters. Any inefficiency can be traced to one or other of the following causes:

(a) Insufficient pre-contract preparation of the particulars of the work to be carried out.

(b) Extensive variation orders after the contract is placed.

(c) Indiscriminate competition tending to place work in the hands of those builders who adopt the lowest standards.

(d) Indefinite relationship between the general contractor and the various sub-contractors nominated by the architect.

25. Much depends on the building owner. His business is to choose a good architect, to keep in close touch with him, and to give him full opportunities of doing his work under the best conditions.

This is by no means always done. The average building owner waits a long time before deciding to put up a new building. Once he makes up his mind to do so he is impatient to receive sketch drawings and close estimates of the cost. Often he thinks that the obtaining of tenders is the only way by which he can satisfy himself as to cost and he presses the architect and quantity surveyor to get the contract fixed. The contract price in these circumstances contains

---

* In Scotland the ordinary practice is that the building owner selects separate contractors for each of the principal trades.

a large number of provisional items which may prove to be quite unreliable; but this does not dissuade the building owner from entering into a contract as he often thinks that the sooner the work can be commenced upon the site the sooner the job will be finished.

There could be no greater mistake. The result of a rushed job of this sort is that nobody has really thought out the details; the owner and the architect, neither of whom has had the opportunity of studying the plans in detail, frequently change their minds; all sorts of improvements, mistakes and difficulties are discovered as the job goes on. The architect is constantly forced to instruct the builder to make variations from the original contract, each one of which causes delay and extra cost, and gives rise to claims for additional payments by the builder.

Another result is that the contract is usually signed long before the details of the various sub-contracts have been settled, and indeed before the architect, who takes responsibility for selecting many of the sub-contractors, has even decided which firms he intends to nominate. The contractor, therefore, when he signs the contract, does not know when each sub-contractor will be ready to begin his job, what his needs will be nor how long it will take him to finish. No reliable time and progress schedule can be made and no effective planning of the work is possible.

26. In all cases it is of the utmost importance that full and detailed drawings, specifications, bills of quantities and estimates should be prepared before the main contract is let, and that subsequent alterations should be reduced to a minimum.

The owner should insist on the completion of detailed drawings and specifications by the architect and should himself do his thinking and make his final decisions on a careful study of these documents; he should not wait to see what the job looks like as it goes up and then change his mind or make new suggestions. The contract drawings and the bills of quantities should accurately represent the work which will ultimately be carried out.

When the owner wishes to insist on undue hurry, the architect should endeavour to convince him of the importance of having time to complete his designs in detail.

The builder should also be in a position to insist on full particulars before starting work, but he is often not listened to, and indeed, even though the inadequately detailed job will cost more, the builder can usually get claims for extras. Where the builder is appointed on the system of cost and fixed fee he may usefully assist as adviser in the early stages.

The responsibility for this rush and inefficiency lies squarely on the shoulders of the building owner. He can prevent it if he wishes. He thinks he is going to get a cheaper and quicker job by rush methods; but he is profoundly mistaken. The work will take longer and will cost more and he is the chief sufferer.

One of the major reforms in the building industry, therefore, is the education of the building owner to adopt businesslike methods in the preliminaries of the contract.

From 'The Placing and Management of Building Contracts', reproduced with the permission of the Controller of Her Majesty's Stationery Office.

Appendix 5

Outline Plan of Work

Plan of Work diagram 1

Stage	Purpose of work and decisions to be reached	Tasks to be done	People directly involved	Usual terminology
A. Inception	To prepare general outline of requirements and plan future action	Set up client organisation for briefing; consider requirements, appoint architect	All client interests, architect	**Briefing**
B. Feasibility	To provide the client with an appraisal and recommendation in order that he may determine the form in which the project is to proceed, ensuring that it is feasible, functionally, technically and financially	Carry out studies of user requirements, site conditions, planning, design, and cost, etc., as necessary to reach decisions	Clients' representatives, architects, engineers, and QS according to nature of project	
C. Outline Proposals	To determine general approach to layout, design and construction in order to obtain authoritative approval of the client on the outline proposals and accompanying report	Develop the brief further; carry out studies on user requirements, technical problems, planning, design and costs, as necessary to reach decisions	All client interests, architects, engineers, QS and specialists as required	**Sketch Plans**

Stage	Purpose	Tasks to be done	People directly involved	
D. Scheme Design	To complete the brief and decide on particular proposals, including planning arrangement appearance, constructional method, outline specification, and cost, and to obtain all approvals	Final development of the brief, full design of the project by architect, preliminary design by engineers, preparation of cost plan and full explanatory report; submission of proposals for all approvals	All client interests, architects, engineers, QS and specialists and all statutory and other approving authorities	
Brief should not be modified after this point				
E. Detail Design	To obtain final decision on every matter related to design, specification, construction and cost	Full design of every part and component of the building by collaboration of all concerned; complete cost checking of designs	Architects, QS, engineers and specialists, contractor (if appointed)	**Working Drawings**
Any further change in location, size, shape, or cost after this time will result in abortive work				
F. Production Information	To prepare production information and make final detailed decisions to carry out work	Preparation of final production information, i.e., drawings, schedules and specifications	Architects, engineers and specialists, contractor (if appointed)	
G. Bills of Quantities	To prepare and complete all information and arrangements for obtaining tender	Preparation of Bills of Quantities and tender documents	Architects, QS, contractor (if appointed)	
H. Tender Action	Action as recommended in NJCC Code of Procedure for Selective Tendering 1972*	Action as recommended in NJCC Code of Procedure for Selective Tendering 1972*	Architects, QS, engineers, contractor, client	
J. Project Planning	To enable the contractor to programme the work in accordance with contract conditions; brief site inspectorate; and make arrangements to commence work on site	Action in accordance with The Management of Building Contracts* and Diagram 9	Contractor, sub-contractors	**Site Operations**

Plan of Work diagram – continued

Stage	Purpose of work and decisions to be reached	Tasks to be done	People directly involved	Usual terminology
K. Operations on Site	To follow plans through to practical completion of the building	Action in accordance with The Management of Building Contracts* and Diagram 10	Architects, engineers, contractors, sub-contractors, QS, client	
L. Completion	To hand over the building to the client for occupation, remedy any defects, settle the final account, and complete all work in accordance with the contract	Action in accordance with The Management of Building Contracts* and Diagram 11	Architects, engineers, contractor, QS, client	
M. Feedback	To analyse the management, construction and performance of the project	Analysis of job records; inspection of completed building; studies of building in use	Architect, engineers, QS, contractor, client	

*The publications Code of Procedure for Selective Tendering (NJCC 1972) and Management of Building Contracts (NJCC 1970) are published by RIBA Publications Limited, London, for the NJCC.

Appendix 6
Extract from the *Client's Guide*

Stage D: Scheme design

4. Decisions required

It is clearly vital that before the client gives approval he is not merely satisfied with the scheme design but fully understands it. To help the client, the architect team may prepare models or perspective drawings. These should include a proper portrayal of the building in relation to its surroundings, for a building that is well designed in itself does not necessarily blend harmoniously with its surroundings. If this fuller presentation reveals that approval of the outline proposals was based on an inadequate appreciation, the client should nevertheless ask his professional advisers to prepare an alternative scheme design. Although a request for an alternative scheme design is bound to cost time and money, the cost of any alteration to the scheme design at this stage will still be small compared with that of making changes later.

In exceptional circumstances such as a fundamental change in the client's requirements or resources, it may become necessary to alter the brief regardless of what stage the job has reached. However, there would need to be overwhelming advantages to justify the loss of time and the additional costs thereby incurred.

Approval of the final scheme design marks the watershed of the design phase. Every requirement should have been worked out within the cost plan and agreed by all concerned, and it is normally unwise and certainly expensive to alter the design after this. About half of the design team's work goes into the following stage – the translation of the scheme design into working drawings and specification notes which between them exactly describe every detail of the building's construction – and much of this work will have to be done again from the beginning if any change is made in the scheme design after it has been approved.

Subsequent stages

1. Further action by the client

The further action that the client should take after approval of the scheme design is to proceed with such matters as finalising the detailed financial arrangements to pay the contractor at the necessary stages, during and after construction, and the selection and ordering of equipment in consultation with the architect, and looking ahead to the arrangements for occupying the building as a whole or by stages.

2. Second application for statutory consents and detailed approvals (II)

The obtaining of consents and approvals is nowadays often almost a continuous process through the design stages. However, it may well be appropriate for the architect to make his submission to the local authority for detailed building regulations and planning consents now on such items as appearance and materials and also proposed solutions on such questions as fire escapes and access for car parking.

3. Detailed design and production drawings: Plan of work Stage E

When the client has approved the scheme design, the design team can embark on the detailed design of the project. The purpose of this work is to obtain a final decision on every matter relating to the design, specification, construction and cost. Every part and component of the building is now fully designed by the design team and a complete check of the designs carried out. After this stage any further change in locations, size, shape or cost will result in abortive work, and should therefore be avoided if at all possible.

4. Production information: Plan of work Stage F

This is followed by the preparation of production information in the form of drawings, schedules, specifications and any other information needed to convey to the contractors, sub-contractors and suppliers precisely what is required for every detail of the building. During this stage the demolition of any buildings on the site may also be arranged.

5. Contract documentation, specification and bills of quantities: Plan of work Stage G

Under the traditional competitive contract procedure, the quantity surveyor will now go on to prepare from the production drawings, in accordance with the designer's specification, the 'bills of quantities' on which the contractor and the specialist sub-contractors will be invited to tender. If the contractor has not already been selected, the architect in conjunction with the quantity surveyor will recommend a list of main contractors suitable for the particular project well before the date envisaged for inviting tenders.

6. Tendering: Plan of work Stage H

Contractors vary widely in financial and technical resources, size of organisation and managerial competence, but the architect will be able to judge which firms are most likely to be capable of making an efficient job of a project of any given type and scale and to advise the client accordingly. The best guarantee of a satisfactory contract is often the mutual understanding born of previous successful co-operation between the architect and a contractor. Selection of the contractor under competitive tendering should be carried out in accordance with the procedures recommended by the NJCC in its *Code of Procedure for Selective Tendering*.

7. Site operations – Project planning, operations on site and completion: Plan of work Stages J–L

The remaining stages of the project are concerned with the operations on site. Having been selected, the contractor has to plan his programme of work in accordance with the contract conditions. By this time the client will have made preparations to fulfil the financial arrangements and sign the contract documents, to make necessary insurance arrangements and to prepare to hand the site over to the contractor. Meanwhile his professional advisers will have held the first project meeting with the contractor to which the client or his representative will also have contributed.

Appendix 7

29. Visiting the site

The contract gives the builder possession of the site and responsibility for the works on it while building operations are in progress, and the client's rights are conditioned by these agreements. The client, therefore, must not embark on any operations either on the site or in the buildings without prior agreement with the architect or engineer and the builder. As far as possible any such operations should be avoided until 'handover' has taken place, otherwise the builder's

. . . on no account say anything that could be construed as an instruction

responsibility for security and progress may diminish – with possible financial embarrassment to the client. The client will, no doubt, wish to visit the site from time to time to see how the work is progressing, but he should make a point of arranging such visits through (and preferably in company with) his designer. If he should at any time be on the site by himself, he must on no account say anything to anybody that could be construed as an instruction. It is fundamental to the efficient management of any undertaking that instructions should come through one channel only, and in a building operation that channel *must* be the designer. If the client has any point to make he should put it to the designer, who will look into its implications in terms of cost, design, and delay and discuss them with him before giving any formal instruction to the builder.

30. No change of mind

It cannot be too strongly emphasised that the cost and delay which the client will have to bear if he insists on a departure from the brief after building has started may well be out of proportion to the advantages he may gain, unless some major change has occurred in his circumstances and requirements since the sketch design was approved. The work on the site is the outcome of months of planning, scheduling, ordering and instruction. Any alteration,

Change of mind

however slight in itself, makes it necessary to stop, change and remotivate a very complicated and cumbersome mechanism. It undermines morale on the site and weakens the sense of urgency and responsibility in all concerned. Much of the inefficiency of which the building industry is accused might be laid more properly at the door of diligent clients who are anxious to have a first-class job but fail to realise what havoc their second thoughts can cause.